Case
Studies
in Schizophrenia

Case Studies in Schizophrenia

Based on the Readings of Edgar Cayce

David McMillin, M.A.

ARE PRESS

ASSOCIATION FOR
RESEARCH AND
ENLIGHTENMENT

A.R.E. Press   •   Virginia Beach   •   Virginia

A.R.E. Press
Sixty-Eighth & Atlantic Avenue
P.O. Box 656
Virginia Beach, VA 23451-0656

Library of Congress Cataloging-in-Publication Data
McMillin, David.
  Case studies in schizophrenia / by David McMillin, M.A.
  Originally published : Virginia Beach, Va. : Lifeline Press, © 1995.
      p.   cm.
  ISBN 0-87604-382-1 (pbk.)
  1. Schizophrenia—Treatment. 2. Cayce, Edgar, 1877-1945. Edgar Cayce readings. 3. Schizophrenia—Etiology. I. Title.
RC514.M396 1997
616.89'82—dc21   97-3237

Cover design by Richard Boyle

Contents

Introduction

◆

SCHIZOPHRENIA IS THE mental health equivalent of cancer or AIDS. It inflicts one percent of the world's population and costs tens of billions of dollars each year in scarce health care resources. However the statistical profile of this disorder does not convey the personal devastation which schizophrenia wreaks upon the suffering individuals, families, and friends who must endure years of insanity. To lose one's mind is the ultimate dehumanizing experience.

Schizophrenia is a form of psychosis. As such, certain psychotic symptoms such as delusions and hallucinations are inherent in the illness. During the acute phases of the disorder, the afflicted person may be said to be "out of touch with reality." At least out of touch with reality as we know it. This qualifier is important—as we shall see in some of the later chapters. Perhaps in certain cases of schizophrenia, the individual is out of touch with this reality and in touch with transcendent realms.

At any rate, persons will often hear voices perceived as coming from outside of themselves. The voices may be singular or multiple. They will sometimes provide commentary or commands. Less frequently, hallucinations involve the other sensory modalities such as vision and touch.

Delusions refer to abnormalities of thought. For example, someone may believe that he or she is being controlled by a dead person or that his or her thoughts are being broadcast to the external world. Delusions of persecution (paranoia) are also common. The classic paranoid delusion is that you are being pursued by the FBI or some other powerful organization. Being convinced that you are Jesus Christ or some other famous historical personage is a typical delusion of grandiosity. Unless you can walk on water or raise the dead, you will probably have a difficult time convincing a psychiatrist that you really don't need one of the powerful antipsychotic medications used to treat delusional thinking. Good luck!

Emotional responses are often inappropriate or totally lacking in persons suffering from schizophrenia. Not surprisingly, interpersonal functioning is often disturbed—sometimes by social withdrawal—occasionally by excessive closeness. We will take a closer look at the full spectrum of psychological and physical symptoms associated with schizophrenia in the pages which follow.

The Medical Model of Schizophrenia

Generally speaking, medical science views schizophrenia as a problem of neurotransmission in the brain. Neurotransmitters are the chemical messengers which allow nerve cells to communicate with each other. In other words, the biochemistry of the brain is abnormal. Specifically, the neurotransmitter dopamine is the most likely candidate among the twenty-eight or so recognized neurotransmitters.

Contemporary research tends to focus on pathology in specific areas of the brain. The limbic system (in the middle of the brain) and the prefrontal cortex (the front of the brain) are likely areas of pathology.

However, this simplistic view of brain dysfunction is problematic. Research has implicated numerous other major neurotransmitters and areas of the brain in schizophrenia. Furthermore, research has clearly demonstrated that other parts of the nervous system are involved (as well as other systems within the body). Notwithstanding all the research and clinical progress that have been made in this century, schizophrenia is still regarded by modern medicine as an incurable brain disease of unknown causation. The drugs which are used to treat it only suppress symptoms—they do not cure. Many patients respond poorly or not at all to these powerful drugs. In addition, unpleasant and dangerous side effects can complicate drug treatment. Relapse is common.

The Genesis of This Book

A few years ago, while in graduate school studying clinical psychology, I rediscovered the psychic readings of Edgar Cayce. I had been aware of this vast collection of information for many years. I knew that Edgar Cayce had given many readings for persons suffering the full range of physical pathology. I was also aware of the "life" readings which discussed past lives and astrological influences. I was even cognizant that he had given a few readings for persons suffering mental and emotional problems. I had reviewed some of the readings which addressed mental illnesses such as schizophrenia and depression. One of the prominent themes which ran through these readings was the concept of incoordination between the nervous systems of the body. I didn't know what Cayce meant by "incoordination between the nervous systems," and like much of the information in the readings I filed it away wondering if someday it would make sense.

You can imagine my amazement when the professor in a graduate course in clinical biopsychology began talking about the physical pathology associated with schizophrenia in just the same terms that Cayce had used decades earlier in his readings. The instructor spoke of the abundant research literature which clearly established the incoordination in nervous system functioning in schizophrenia. He went on to note that this was one of the few things that we know for certain about schizophrenia. Our level of ignorance of this serious illness is almost overwhelming. Naturally, I was curious and wanted to know more. Upon request, my instructor provided me with a list of articles documenting nervous system incoordination in schizophrenia. I was on my way. I didn't know where I was going, but it felt right and I trusted it.

My academic research resulted in a master's thesis entitled *Research and Clinical Implications of Autonomic Nervous System Involvement in Schizophrenia*. In my thesis, I blended the psychological and psychiatric literature with my understanding of the

Cayce material. After graduation, I researched deeper into the Cayce readings and expanded my thesis into a book entitled *The Treatment of Schizophrenia: A Holistic Approach Based on the Readings of Edgar Cayce.*

While looking more closely at the readings, I was intrigued to find that Edgar Cayce had actually given hundreds of readings on mental illness. With this realization, I determined within myself to see if this material was relevant to contemporary clinical practice. While modern therapeutic approaches provide varying degrees of symptomatic relief for mental illness, the fact remains that we do not know for certain the cause, nor do we have the cure for any of the major mental illnesses. Maybe the Cayce perspective could make a contribution. I simply wanted to find out for myself if Edgar Cayce's trance-induced observations were true, in any practical sense. If they were valid, the therapeutic implications were enormous.

I set out to apply the information. Without going into detail, I will simply note that I have found the Cayce information extremely helpful in the treatment of major mental illness, including schizophrenia. In a certain sense, this book is one of my attempts at application of the material.

The Purpose of This Book

The purpose of this book is to make the information provided by Edgar Cayce about schizophrenia more widely accessible to persons seeking alternative perspectives on this illness. Such a person may be a family member or friend of someone who has been diagnosed as having schizophrenia. Or perhaps individuals carrying the diagnosis may wish to view the problem from an alternative perspective. To increase accessibility, the style is nontechnical. Readers desiring a more academic presentation of this material may wish to consider the earlier work entitled *The Treatment of Schizophrenia: A Holistic Approach Based on the Readings of Edgar Cayce* (see Appendix).

The structure of most chapters will be built around a group of case studies which illustrate an important concept about schizophrenia. Typically, I will include relevant information from other sources such as medical research and the clinical literature. Additional information from the readings may also be cited when available.

The first part of the book will address the causes of schizophrenia. In recognition of the substantial biological dimension of schizophrenia, this section might be viewed as more "mainstream" in its orientation.

The second part will digress to a more expansive consideration of the subject. It will address the context of the human experience for persons suffering major mental illness. In other words, we will consider the meaning of schizophrenia. The position adopted will be defined as holism—a viewpoint which emphasizes the whole self—body, mind, and spirit. From this view, we will hopefully be able to make sense of the causes of schizophrenia cited in the earlier chapters. In part, holism as represented in the Cayce readings states that body, mind, and spirit connect through definite anatomical centers in the body. Specifically, mind interfaces through the nervous systems and spirit manifests through the glands of the body. I regard these anatomical structures as key elements in the "body-soul connection." This connection is vulnerable to insult from a variety of factors (such as spinal injury). So as you read Part One and note the preponderance of spinal injuries and glandular dysfunction, be aware that these causes relate to a bigger picture of human functioning—the body/soul connection.

Hence, Part Two will go beyond physical pathology to examine the role of the kundalini energy (the "life force" present in each living being), reincarnation, and possession. Hopefully, readers will find the presentation of these extraordinary topics to be sensible and consistent with the material discussed in Part One.

The Work of Edgar Cayce

For readers unfamiliar with the work of Edgar Cayce, the following background information may be helpful. Edgar Cayce was born on March 18, 1877, on a farm near Hopkinsville, Kentucky. His childhood was marked by paranormal experiences such as seeing and speaking to recently deceased relatives and sleeping with his head on textbooks to memorize school lessons. His abilities as a psychic diagnostician were utilized during his early twenties when he developed a gradual paralysis of the throat. Medical doctors were unable to provide relief. As a last resort, he allowed a friend to hypnotize him so that he could reestablish the state of consciousness that he had utilized as a child when he memorized his school books. From this trance state, he was able to diagnosis his condition and prescribe treatments which remedied the problem. Cayce was hesitant to use his ability for others because he felt responsible for the information. He was concerned that the suggested treatments might have harmful effects. Consequently, many of the early beneficiaries of his services were desperate cases, often given up by medical doctors. Working within the medical establishment, in partnership with various physicians who utilized his gift, Cayce felt assured that his unusual ability would do no harm. After several years as a professional photographer and part-time psychic, Cayce devoted his life to giving readings.

Cayce refused to "cash in" on this ability by performing on stage or offering his services to the highest bidder. Rather, he chose to offer his services to those in need on a donation basis. Consequently, many readings were provided free or for nominal donations. Cayce suffered financial hardship for most of his life and apparently accepted monetary austerity as his karma for having squandered resources in a previous life.

As an indication of Cayce's interest in providing help to persons suffering from physical illness, most of his psychic readings were given in response to health issues. The remainder cover virtually every area of human endeavor, from religion and philosophy to business and international affairs.

The readings addressing mental health are particularly relevant to the present work and cover the entire field of psychopathology. There exist numerous readings on psychosis, depression, anxiety, dementia, personality disorders, developmental disorders, etc. Other aspects of psychology such as learning and memory, the nature of personality, perception, psychosocial development, consciousness, the meaning of sleep, etc., are interspersed throughout the readings and provide intriguing perspectives on these concepts.

Apart from the content of Cayce's readings, the trance process itself is a fascinating facet of Cayce's work. Harmon Bro, in his excellent biography of Cayce entitled *A Seer Out of Season*, provides a glimpse into the trance procedure and the physical context of the readings:

What took place in the morning and afternoon trance sessions, in the months that followed when I heard and took notes on some six hundred of Cayce's readings, was a profound shock. Nothing could adequately prepare one for the amount of swift helpfulness that flowed from the unconscious man. His outward procedures were simple enough. Cayce sat on his plain green studio couch in his cheerful windowed study, across the room from his desk and little portable typewriter. He prayed, then lay down and step by step went unconscious. He spoke in measured address about each person or need to which his wife, sitting beside him, quietly directed his attention. After an hour or more of discourse and questions which his secretary recorded in shorthand, he came swiftly back to consciousness, remembering nothing of what he had said, and got up to resume the activities of his busy correspondence and office. It was all done in broad daylight and simplicity, as naturally as if he were still taking portraits in a photographic studio. But the plainness of the process did not take away the jolt of seeing him accomplish day after day what our culture said was impossible.

Although some of the early readings were not recorded, over 14,000 were stenographically transcribed and have been preserved by the Association for Research and Enlightenment (A.R.E.) in Virginia Beach, Virginia. Recognizing the need for confidentiality, each reading is assigned a number corresponding to the person or group requesting information. The identifying number is followed by another number designating the sequence of the reading. For example, a reading cited as 182-6 indicates that this reading is the sixth in a series of readings for an individual or group designated as 182.

I will include abundant examples of readings directly from Cayce's work to provide readers a first-hand glimpse into his psychic technique. In this way, I intend to let the readings speak for themselves to the fullest extent possible. I will provide parallel information from modern research and other important sources. I will also include additional background information from family or medical sources to provide a context for considering each case.

At least a couple of dozen individuals suffering from schizophrenia (or its diagnostic precursor, dementia praecox) sought psychic readings from Edgar Cayce. The readings consistently emphasized the strong biological dimension of this disorder and graphically described the brain dysfunctions which modern medical research is uncovering. Yet, the readings typically viewed this brain degeneration as an effect rather than the primary cause. Quite often other systems were cited as being the basic cause. For example, the endocrine glands and autonomic nervous system were portrayed as major sources of pathology.

In other words, the brain does not exist in isolation. To maintain itself, it requires a constant supply of nutrients and the continual removal of metabolic waste. Without the support of the rest of the body, brain functioning degenerates. The causes and treatment of this degenerative process will be explored in the case studies which follow.

The Perennial Philosophy of the Cayce Readings

The work of Edgar Cayce does not exist in a philosophical vacuum. Rather, throughout the ages numerous individuals have manifested similar paranormal gifts while expounding an expansive view of the human condition. This view has been called the *Perennial Philosophy*. Author Ken Wilber has traced the perennial philosophy through ages of human activity:

> But there is a much more sophisticated view of the relation of humanity and Divinity, a view held by the great majority of the truly gifted theologians, philosophers, sages, and even scientists of various times. Known in general as the "perennial philosophy" (a name coined by Leibnitz), it forms the esoteric core of Hinduism, Buddhism, Taoism, Sufism, and Christian mysticism, as well as being embraced, in whole or part, by individual intellects ranging from Spinoza to Albert Einstein, Schopenhauer to Jung, William James to Plato. Further, in its purest form it is not at all anti-science but, in a special sense, trans-science or even ante-science, so that it can happily coexist with, and certainly complement, the hard data of the pure sciences. This is why, I believe, that so many of the truly brilliant scientists have always flirted with, or totally embraced, the perennial philosophy, as witness Einstein, Schrodinger, Eddington, David Bohm, Sir James Jeans, even Isaac Newton.

Aldous Huxley advocates a similar perspective of the perennial philosophy which emphasizes the "tripartite" quality of human nature. Significantly, the tripartite "body/mind/spirit" interface is a major theme in the Cayce readings and provides the foundation for the "holistic" perspective advocated in this book.

The Perennial Philosophy is primarily concerned with the one, divine Reality substantial to the manifold world of things and lives and minds . . . In other words, there is a hierarchy of the real . . . But all of these men, even La Rochefoucauld, even Machiavelli, were aware of certain facts which twentieth-century psychologists have chosen to ignore—the fact that human nature is tripartite, consisting of a spirit as well as of a mind and body; the fact that we live on the borderline between two worlds, the temporal and the eternal, the physical-vital-human and the divine . . . Man's final end, the purpose of his existence, is to love, know and be united with the immanent and transcendent Godhead.

Recognition of Cayce's work as being representative of the perennial philosophy—as an extension of a tradition of ideas and practices which underlie most of the world's major religions and philosophies—is essential for a full appreciation of his contribution. From this perspective, he cannot simply be dismissed as a religious fanatic seeking to establish an esoteric cult; a crackpot practicing medical quackery and milking desperate innocents of their resources; or a deluded psychotic experiencing pathological trance states resulting in thousands of incoherent, implausible psychic readings. To the contrary, Cayce's life and work exemplify a long and respected tradition among the great cultures of the world. Although his beliefs have a definite Judeo/Christian orientation, his recognition of the continuity of consciousness, including such Eastern concepts as karma and reincarnation, attest to the scope of his perspective.

We will take up the concept of the "continuity of consciousness" in the second portion of this book when we consider the "transpersonal" aspects of schizophrenia. By transpersonal, I simply refer to those dimensions of the human experience which transcend the personal sense of self (or the personality/ego). These dimensions involve mental and spiritual aspects which stretch our view of the human experience. Certain concepts of the perennial philosophy such as kundalini (the "life force"), reincarnation, and karma are essential for a full consideration of major mental illness.

In other words, human beings are more than biological machines. Complex mental illnesses such as schizophrenia naturally involve more than biological pathology. Furthermore, the effective treatment of schizophrenia involves more that physical interventions. As we shall see, Edgar Cayce adopted a "holistic" approach to healing the person suffering from schizophrenia. Holism means that the whole person is taken into consideration. From Cayce's perspective, the whole person is a unity or entity involving physical, mental, and spiritual aspects. Along with physical/biological therapies, the mental and spiritual dimensions of treatment are regarded as crucial ingredients in a comprehensive treatment model. The case studies which follow exemplify Edgar Cayce's holistic approach.

PART I

THE BIOPSYCHOLOGY
OF SCHIZOPHRENIA

1

Dementia Praecox

◆

SCHIZOPHRENIA IS AN exceedingly complex illness. In fact, if you were to have the opportunity to observe an ample number of individuals diagnosed as schizophrenic, you might find yourself wondering if they were all suffering from the same disorder. Your observation would not be unreasonable. It is widely accepted by leading researchers that there is considerable variability within schizophrenia as it is currently defined.

Many researchers have interpreted this variability to mean that schizophrenia may consist of a group of related disorders. This confusing situation has arisen, in part at least, from our ignorance of the causes of schizophrenia. The first part of this book will examine the sources of variability in schizophrenia by considering some of the causes noted in the Edgar Cayce readings. In a sense, we will be allowed to lift the curtain of our ignorance—to peek behind the veil of puzzling biological, psychological, and spiritual factors which have been implicated as causes of schizophrenia.

To help us understand the nature of schizophrenia, we will take a glance down the historical avenue leading to our current diagnostic dilemma. In considering the history of insanity, we may gain a deeper understanding of our subject. Such a review will also help to set the stage for Edgar Cayce's perspective on this devastating disorder. The term schizophrenia was created by Alfred Bleuler in 1911. Literally, it refers to a split between thought and emotion which Bleuler regarded as the hallmark of the illness. Bleuler's interpretation reveals a psychological emphasis which has persisted until recent times. The focus has been on mental and emotional processes. Naturally, this viewpoint was strongly influenced by the early popularity of the psychoanalytic movement in this country. Hence, aberrant childhood developmental stages were sometimes cited as a cause of schizophrenia.

Can faulty potty training cause schizophrenia? Not likely, yet psychoanalytic theorists found in schizophrenia a fertile ground for hypotheses. One of the strongest and most persistent views focused on poor mothering as the source of the problem. Consequently, guilt-ridden mothers suffered through years of "mom bashing" because their child became afflicted with schizophrenia later in life. Modern scientific research has largely debunked this unfortunate way of thinking about schizophrenia.

During the 1950s, the discovery of the antipsychotic medications shifted the focus to the biological dimensions of the illness. The discovery of the antipsychotic properties of certain drugs (such as Thorazine) can be traced back to the French physician Henri Laborit. Laborit was looking for a drug to prevent a drop in blood pressure during surgery. Although the drug he used failed in that respect, it did have noticeable sedative effects. Subsequent research by French psychiatrists was by trial and error—they gave the drug to persons suffering from a wide range of disorders to see if it had any effect. The medication had powerful calming effects on agitated psychotic patients and thus: "The first powerful drug available to treat serious mental illness was discovered in much the same way as was penicillin: by accident. The discovery was the happy consequence of a chance finding being observed by a person with a fertile mind who could recognize its larger implications." The preceding observation was noted by Nancy Andreasen, M.D., Ph.D., a leading researcher in the field of mental illness.

Modern brain-scan technology has further bolstered the biological focus in schizophrenia. Through a variety of techniques, scientists have noted brain abnormalities in many persons diagnosed as schizophrenic. Some of the strongest evidence comes from studies which document an enlargement of the brain's ventricles in cases of schizophrenia. The ventricles carry cerebrospinal fluid. It is thought that an enlargement of the ventricles results from a degeneration of brain tissue itself. In a sense, the flexible ventricles may expand to take up the space left when nerve cells in the brain deteriorate and shrink in volume. As with most research in schizophrenia, the brain-scan literature is complex and variable. We can only hope that improved technology and further research can unravel the details in this fascinating and significant area of investigation.

So this is where we find ourselves today, in the midst of a biological revolution which has transformed psychiatry. Consequently, psychological explanations have taken a back seat to physiological theories.

In a sense, we have returned to an earlier viewpoint. Previous to Bleuler's psychological rendition, psychiatrists had used the term dementia praecox as a diagnostic label for chronically psychotic patients. This term has a strong biological flavor because dementia refers to irreversible brain degeneration and praecox means precocious or early. Since the illness often manifested during the late teens and early twenties, this designation was quite literal as a descriptive diagnosis.

Emil Kraepelin, the father of modern psychiatry, was very influential in clarifying the meaning of the major mental illnesses including dementia praecox. He believed that dementia praecox involved brain degeneration which most likely resulted from a metabolic disorder. Kraepelin's insights are more than mere historical curiosity. Modern psychiatry has shifted its focus away from psychological theorizing and is currently re-examining the seminal work of Kraepelin and the early biological psychiatrists.

So while the emphasis has shifted back to a biological perspective similar to Kraepelin's concept of dementia praecox, we have kept the term schizophrenia in use. We have experienced an almost constant revision of diagnostic criteria and types of schizophrenia, yet the term remains. However the problem of variability still plagues medical research. This is particularly evident in the problem of replication in research studies. For example, one team of researchers may report a significant finding, yet other researchers are unable to confirm the important finding in follow-up studies. Thus many researchers have come to the conclusion that schizophrenia actually consists of a group of related disorders. Each study may use a slightly (or greatly) different blend of schizophrenic subtypes. Consequently, findings would also be diverse and difficult to replicate. Replication is so important because it is fundamental to the scientific process. Without replication, we cannot know if any particular research finding is true or simply the result of a faulty experiment.

I have made this effort to discuss the diversity of the population of individuals diagnosed as suffering from schizophrenia for an important reason. The Cayce readings were decades ahead of current research in discussing the causes of this diversity. Therefore, it is imperative that readers be aware of this acknowledged variance before proceeding to the case studies which follow. To be sure, there are many causes of schizophrenia and they will be addressed in this book.

Likewise, I have emphasized the strong biological aspect of schizophrenia for an important reason. While both terms (dementia praecox and schizophrenia) were in use by the health care professionals of his era, Edgar Cayce consistently preferred the term dementia praecox. Although several individuals came to Cayce with a diagnosis of schizophrenia, he did not use that term when diagnosing their condition.

Cayce's reluctance to describe persons as schizophrenic may have involved more than diagnostic obsolescence. Dementia praecox was a useful diagnostic category. It affirmed organic degeneration and deteriorating course. These were clinical and pathological realities which the readings graphically described.

On the other hand, Bleuler's schizophrenia was conceptualized as a psychological construct inferring splitting of the personality (i.e., a splitting of thought and emotion). From Cayce's perspective, this description apparently did not adequately fit the illness. Such a vague and insubstantial concept may have been deemed unsuitable for the condition of those seeking Cayce's help.

So while modern psychiatry has generally deferred to a more biological stance which is reminiscent of Kraepelin's and Cayce's perspectives (dementia praecox), the term schizophrenia has remained part of the psychiatric lexicon. Many researchers and clinicians have decried its use calling it a "wastebasket" diagnosis. It has come to include so much that its meaning has become muddled. The medical establishment has sought to remedy this problem by tightening up the diagnostic criteria for schizophrenia. Theorists have sought to define the subgroups with labels such as reactive, endogenous, process, type I and type II schizophrenia, etc. Some researchers have even created the classification of "Kraepelinian schizophrenia" to call attention to the foresight of modern psychiatry's founder. These attempts are clearly oriented toward clarifying the biological nature of the illness.

This is where the work of Edgar Cayce may make a significant contribution. Apparently, he was able to "see" the physiological condition involving nervous system degeneration. Furthermore, he claimed to be able to look backwards through time and find the source of the problem.

"Dementia Praecox (as Some Have Diagnosed It)"

Mr. [271] was about thirty years old when he developed schizophrenic symptoms. Reading 271-1 described his condition in explicit anatomical terms. Cayce's account predated by several decades contemporary models of schizophrenia which emphasize brain dysfunction. This reading given on February 13, 1933, noted that "In a general manner the condition may be termed dementia praecox (as some have diagnosed it)." Obviously, the entranced Cayce was already tuned in to the problematic nature of diagnosis. "As some have diagnosed it" affirms the relative nature of psychiatric classification.

He went on to note that such diagnoses were variable. He said, "but the type and nature of the disturbance—physically and mentally, as we find—would indicate that" help might be afforded if certain treatments were provided. Again, the wording is important. He is saying that even within the relatively specific diagnosis of dementia praecox, there could be various types with different natures. In the chapters which follow we will have the opportunity to closely examine these types and natures.

However, the connecting thread which ran through all the cases which Cayce diagnosed as dementia praecox was inevitable brain pathology which modern medical science is so keen on investigating. In this particular case, he cited, "softening of cell cord and brain tissue."

He then commented on the source of the disorder. He traced the pathology all the way back to the womb. The cause was:

Pressures and incoordinations that are shown from prenatal conditions, and the activities in the physical that have brought about and indicate the abrasions to the nervous system in such a manner as to make for a . . . condition existent as diagnosed . . .

The expression "prenatal conditions" is vague in this context. In certain cases it included problems with gestation. In other cases, prenatal conditions referred to genetic factors. Sometimes it was suggestive of "karmic" factors (we will discuss these concepts in later chapters). The only thing we can be certain of here is that Cayce was stating that the problem originated before birth.

The explicit descriptions of nervous system pathology were repeated in subsequent readings. For example, in reading 271-5 Cayce described how there was a problem with "those glands that secrete fluids which in the circulation sustain and maintain the reaction fluid in the nerve channels themselves." Considering that this reading was given on May 1st of 1933, it has a remarkably modern ring to it. He seems to be describing the basis for a breakdown in nerve-cell functioning—perhaps in neurotransmission itself (the process of passing nerve impulses between nerve cells via chemical messengers).

A little later in this reading he went on to describe how the electrical treatments were causing the nervous system to regenerate itself. Cayce noted that:

. . . there is being sent out from these [nerve] ganglia those infinitesimal feelers, as it were, that will gradually make connections with those ganglia and centers in the system that have been destroyed by the reactions in the system which destroyed gland functioning for the creating of these fluids . . .

The electrotherapy treatments just mentioned were of two natures. The primary therapy for regenerating the nervous system was the Wet Cell Battery carrying a gold chloride solution. For a period of three to five weeks, the contact plates of this appliance were to be positioned directly over key ganglia in the nervous system. Cayce said that the low form of electrical energy would allow the vibrations of the gold solution to be assimilated into the body. The glands would thus be stimulated to secrete the fluids required by the nervous system. The combination of these secretions and the direct electrical stimulation would lead to restoration of nervous system functioning—a literal "rebuilding" of the nervous systems. I want to be clear about what Cayce meant when he used the expression "rebuild" the nervous system (in certain cases of dementia, he actually said that one could rebuild a brain). He was not saying that new nerve cells would be created. Rather, that the existing degenerated nerve tissue would be nourished and stimulated to regain a normal healthy state (to send out "from these [nerve] ganglia those infinitesimal feelers"). This was not viewed as a quick or easy process. It would require patience and persistent application of a variety of related therapies which we will be considering in the case studies of this book.

The second form of electrotherapy recommended for this young man was a device referred to as the Radio-Active Appliance. The Radio-Active Appliance (also referred to as the Impedance Device) was frequently recommended by Cayce for the treatment of a variety of problems. It was said to function strictly at the vibratory level working directly with the low electrical energy or life force of the physical body. The readings state that this appliance works with the same vibrational energy as the Wet Cell Battery but is less powerful.

The Radio-Active Appliance was often suggested to relax and coordinate the systems of the body. The readings insisted that the appliance did not produce any energy, rather it utilized the body's own vibratory energies by redirecting them to establish equilibrium.

The term "radio-active" in no way signifies atomic radiation of a toxic nature. In fact, the vibrational energy associated with this appliance cannot be measured with current scientific technology. The original designation was intended to describe the interaction of the appliance and a subtle energy or "life force" (i.e., like a radio and radio waves). The name was later changed to Impedance Device to avoid confusion as to the nature of the energies involved.

The amazing thing about both these two forms of electrotherapy is how mild they are. Most persons feel little or no sensation while using them.

Several other physical therapies were recommended in addition to electrotherapy. Specific recommendations for diet and exercise were provided. A gentle spinal massage was to be given in the evening when Mr. [271] was ready for bed. During the massage and as he was drifting into sleep, suggestions were to be given:

. . . during such periods [of massage] (for most often we would find the body would gradually fall into that state of near

between the waking and sleeping state) make gentle suggestions that QUIET, REST, PEACE, HAPPINESS, JOY, DEVELOP-
MENTS IN EVERY MANNER THAT ARE CONSTRUCTIVE
PHYSICALLY AND MENTALLY, will come to the body through
its rest period! Or, the suggestion to the deeper portion of the
subconscious forces of the body.

Cayce referred to this natural form of hypnosis as suggestive
therapeutics. Suggestive therapeutics is a powerful hypnotic technique for dealing with behavioral problems and facilitating the healing process. Suggestive therapeutics was often recommended in
cases of major mental illness.
The application of suggestive therapeutics is simple. Because
most people were unfamiliar with the techniques for inducing a
hypnotic trance, the readings advised that suggestions be provided
during the various physical treatments. At that time, the person was
usually in a relaxed receptive state of mind. Thus during the electrotherapy, massage, and manipulations the caregiver was directed to
talk to the patient in a calm, firm voice; giving positive suggestions
for physical, mental, and spiritual healing. The suggestions could
also be directed towards undesirable behaviors or lack of cooperation.
As was the case with Mr. [271], the readings also frequently advised that bedtime be utilized as a time for suggestive therapeutics.
During the first few minutes of sleep, a slumbering individual is in a
hypnogogic state and is very open to suggestion. This form of suggestive therapeutics is sometimes referred to as presleep suggestions.
As with all forms of suggestive therapeutics, presleep suggestions
are made to the person's unconscious mind and should be positive
and constructive in tone and content. The particular content of the
suggestion for this man was changed in reading 271-5:

Then, in the suggestions that we would make when the body
is sleeping, resting, there should be had those that will make
for the better creative forces; for to reach the subconscious self
it must be without the physical-mental self. See? Yet in the
waking state, in the activity, there will be seen those reactions
occasionally; at first possibly once a week, possibly once a day,
possibly several times a day, dependent upon how persistent
the suggestions are made with the active forces that are being

set out in the system from the physical angle. See? Change the suggestions, then, in this manner, or to this:

THERE WILL BE, IN THE WHOLE OF THE PHYSICAL AND MENTAL BODY, THAT RESPONSE TO THAT CREATIVE ENERGY WHICH IS BEING CARRIED INTO THE SYSTEM. PERFECT COORDINATION WILL COME TO THE BODY. THERE WILL BE NORMAL REACTIONS IN EVERY WAY AND MANNER THROUGH THE CREATIVE FORCES OF DIVINE LOVE THAT IS MANIFEST IN THE HEARTS AND MINDS OF THOSE ABOUT THE BODY.

This should be repeated three to four times, until it has gradually reached the subconscious, or the unconscious, or the consciousness of the living forces that are impelling activity in a distorted condition, as to the balance in the mental forces of [271].

In a sense, you can think of suggestive therapeutics as a form of mental programming similar to computer programming. Only in cases of chronic schizophrenia (i.e., dementia praecox), where there was actual nervous tissue degeneration, the process was more complicated. It was as if both the "hardware" and the "software" of the system would have to re-created. The physical therapies focused on rebuilding the "hardware" (the nerve tissue) while suggestive therapeutics (and a group of "spiritually" oriented therapies which we will discuss presently) were to serve as the "software" or mental program, as it were. In other words, the readings stated that as the nervous system was being rebuilt, it was important to give it constructive information for its new "program."

This brings us to the "spiritual" dimension of therapy. The business of speaking, acting, and even thinking constructively in the presence of a suffering individual might be called manifesting the "fruits of the spirit," to use a biblical expression. In contemporary psychiatric terms, it is called providing a "therapeutic milieu." In other words, the total environment (or milieu) is structured to be therapeutic. For example, the first reading given for Mr. [271] insisted that he be put:

... in an environ that is as of a growth—and the body physically and mentally treated as an individual, a unit, rather than as a class or as a mass consideration ...

At the time of this reading, Mr. [271] was in Pinewood Sanitarium, a private mental institution in Katonah, New York. He was likely receiving better care there than he would have gotten at one of the state mental asylums of that era. And yet he was apparently still being treated as a dementia praecox case (or in today's terminology, a schizophrenia case). Remember that we are speaking of 1933, over twenty years before the antipsychotic medications were introduced. To receive a diagnosis of dementia praecox was essentially a therapeutic "kiss of death." As Cayce noted in a similar case of a twenty-two-year-old man, Mr. [5405]:

> In the present environs, and under the existent shadows, very little may be accomplished for those individuals in authority take little interest in even possibilities, where there have been, and are evidences of this nature or character of dementia praecox . . .

Very often, these persons were simply herded together in locked wards and encouraged to vegetate. Cayce stated the first step in the treatment of this young man was to remove him from the institution and provide him with individual care in a positive, constructive environment. Specifically, he recommended a place with a "clean atmosphere, in plenty of sunshine and out-of-door activity." To implement the treatment plan in a proper environment, Cayce suggested that Mr. [271] be provided:

> . . . with a companion constantly that would make for those engagements mentally and physically in activities that are constructive and yet, with patience and persistence, have those activities carried on in such a way as to make for constructive thinking, constructive activity, both as to the association and as to the speech, and as to the environment.

The recommendation for companion therapy was commonly made in cases of dementia praecox. Cayce was decades ahead of his time in making this recommendation. There are several contemporary psychosocial rehabilitation models using a similar approach. The modern terms for such adjunct caretakers include companions, advocates, counselors, advisors, operatives, attendants, and support persons.

Cayce clearly stated the role of the companion. Naturally, adherence to the treatment plan was a top priority. This was a particularly difficult assignment in the case of [271]. First of all, the man chosen as a companion had no experience in working with persons suffering from mental illness. Even if he had been trained in the social services of his day, it is unlikely that he would have been prepared for some of his assignments. For example, recall the recommendations for suggestive therapeutics. This is not a skill commonly taught to mental health professionals, even in our time.

The use of behavioral modeling was also recommended by Cayce. Behavioral modeling is a term derived from research in social learning theory. It is a well-documented fact that we learn much of our behavior from observing others. This process is fittingly referred to as "observational learning." From a clinical standpoint, therapeutic observational learning can best be accomplished with the aid of a person "modeling" the appropriate behavior—hence the term behavioral modeling. This may all seem painfully obvious to readers. However, keep in mind that these theories and the research which supported them were not accomplished until the 1960s and 1970s. Yet Edgar Cayce was incorporating such concepts into treatment plans thirty to forty years ahead of mainstream psychiatric rehabilitation. Here is a sample of his advice for utilizing behavioral modeling. This excerpt comes from the fifth reading given for [271]:

Q. Is there any way in which to get this body to eat any form of fruit?

A. Gradually. Listen to just what has been given! The body assumes activities and acts by suggestion of everyone around the body! If all around the body eat fruit, the body will gradually eat fruit itself! Isn't that just what we have been saying?

Q. Should I [the companion] insist upon his getting up in the morning, or does it antagonize him?

A. As given, it is best that the body arise as soon as it awakes. Do not antagonize, but suggest! Do so yourself, and the body will get up too!

Note that Cayce is describing behavioral modeling as almost a form of suggestion (i.e., suggestive therapeutics). Instead of words being programmed into the person's mind, behaviors are being suggested. In the same reading, Cayce actually elaborated upon the physiology of how behavioral modeling is incorporated into nervous system patterns. He described how stimuli from the sensory organs were relayed to the rest of the nervous system for processing:

> Hence by speech, by vision, by odor, by feeling, all make a sensitive reaction on a body where there is being electrical stimulation to ganglia to make for connections in their various activities over the system.
>
> Hence it may be easily seen how careful all should be, how much precaution, patience and persistence must be had in making every suggestion; by speech, by sight, by feeling, by vision, by eating, by sleeping, by all senses of the body; to coordinate with the proper balance being made in the system. See?

Remember that the physical therapies (and especially the electrotherapy) were rebuilding the nervous systems. Sensory information was being implanted into the new nerve relays, as it were. Thus all sensory stimuli in the environment, whether it be suggestive therapeutics, behavioral modeling, the cleanliness of the facility, etc., was to be constructive in nature. He stated that if you merely provided the physical therapies without regard for the type of information that was being encoded into the nervous systems, you could end up with a mess. Cayce's view of the therapeutic milieu even included the mass media:

> When reading matter is desired, do not give the body reading matter other than that which is constructive. No gang land. No underworld. Not a great deal of animosity or excitement in the reading matter . . .
>
> Q. Are movies occasionally well for the body?
>
> A. Provided they do not carry that same element of reaction to the mental body as we have indicated [violence]. Those that present reactions of a constructive nature are well.
>
> Remember, you are dealing with mental recuperative forces; and conditions act upon the mind just as would be experienced in the development of a six to eight, to twelve year old child!
>
> But the mind is being rebuilt! Give it the proper things to build upon! else there will be found that the reactions and tendencies will be towards those things destructive, or whatever is taken in the mind.
>
> Speak, act, think constructively about the body! Some may consider it a hard job, but it's worth it . . .

I regard the therapeutic milieu and companion therapy (as presented in the Cayce material) as representing the spiritual aspect of treatment. In order to effectively provide the therapies recommended by Cayce, one has to have a great deal of love for another human being. Call it what you will—use another word if you find the term "spirituality" offensive. Cayce used the biblical expression "fruits of the spirit" to express this dimension of treatment. Spirituality included patience, persistence, kindness, gentleness, and so forth. You get the idea.

And yet, he insisted that the companion maintain certain boundaries and not give into every whim of his charge—"not condoning or allowing the body to have its own mental way, and react to same, but in an even, gentle tone and manner" to provide a constructive environment for healing. The readings tended to view the issue of personal boundaries on an individual basis, taking into consideration the resources at hand. In cases of severe disability, the companion carried a great deal of responsibility in the initial stages of treatment. As the suffering individual gained sanity, more self-responsibility was expected and encouraged.

This approach is similar to modern therapeutic models which place the initial burden of responsibility on professional caretakers (such as the staff of a hospital psychiatric ward or state hospital). As the individual responds to treatment, more self-responsibility is expected. Because some psychiatric patients develop manipulative techniques for avoiding responsibility, the question of how much self-responsibility is appropriate must always be addressed. We will note instances of how Cayce dealt with the issue of balance of responsibility in subsequent chapters. For now, I simply want to point out that this is not an easy assignment. As we shall see, it was not effectively carried out in this case.

Before discussing the outcome in this case, I do want to make a point concerning Cayce's philosophy. I will not go deeply into theory here except to designate Cayce's approach as a prime example of "holism." In fact, Edgar Cayce has often been acknowledged as the "father of modern holistic medicine." Cayce repeatedly insisted that we are each triune beings comprised of body, mind, and spirit. His treatment plans typically reflected this conceptualization of the human condition. Regarding the case of [271], note the emphasis on a holistic treatment plan. The foundation was laid with a strong physical emphasis as one would expect in a case involving neurological impairment. However he went on to prescribe mental and spiritual interventions such as suggestive therapeutics, companion therapy, and therapeutic milieu. This theme of holism is so important, it will be echoed numerous times in various contexts in the following chapters.

The outcome in this case is difficult to assess. Reading 271-7 notes:

> ... there are tendencies towards betterments, and of conditions that may be builded to bring about a much nearer normal reaction in the coordinating of the mental and physical reactions of the body.

The reading went on to discuss that the progress was necessarily slow due to the severity of the condition. Cayce encouraged a continuance of the therapies which were producing the "improvements or the stopping of deterioration in the white matter of the brain impulse." The general tone of this reading is that the neurological deterioration had been halted and modest gains in rebuilding the system were being made. He went on to observe:

> For there are periods when the reactions are near normal. The periods then of what may be termed rationality, in reasoning, are longer; they may not be but a moment longer, but to this experience that may mean many years of sane rationalism, if those moments are taken advantage of.

In reading 271-8, Cayce cautioned that:

> ... while there may not be said to be at present any greater deteriorative forces active in the membranes, or those disorders that disturb the equilibrium of the reactions in nerve systems through the activity of the brain centers, little of a contributory cause to a betterment has been added since last we had the body here.

Apparently the burden of responsibility weighed too heavily on the companion at this point. The small observable gains (and Cayce's assurance that unobservable neurological healing was occurring) were not enough to bolster the morale of the companion. After about four months of struggling to implement Cayce's treatment plan, the companion quit and a new companion was enlisted.

A few weeks later [271] was returned to a mental institution. In a letter dated May 1, 1934, the mother states, "I am glad to tell you that [271] is doing very well . . . He has certainly improved a lot and is contented . . . "

While the readings noted a halting of nerve deterioration in this case, the rebuilding process was apparently not fully achieved. One of the primary stumbling blocks cited in the readings was the lack of application of the electrotherapy. Repeatedly, the companion was chided for not being able to get [271] to accept this therapy. Reading 271-8 did acknowledge the beneficial effects of outdoor physical exercise, yet:

> . . . without . . . the low electrical forces, with those supplies of the minerals necessary to be active in constructive influences in brain tissue and nerve elements of the system . . . [the outdoor activities] are hardly efficient in keeping constructive forces.

The powerful therapeutic effects of minerals such as gold were strongly emphasized in the readings and we will discuss this intriguing topic in later chapters. Evidently, in this case the electrotherapy was not utilized consistently enough to produce the full desired results (although a decided improvement was noted by the mother).

The actual period of treatment in this case was only about five months. Keep in mind the meaning of the term dementia praecox. It referred to a chronic degenerative form of psychosis with actual brain deterioration. To translate this into modern diagnostic context (in which schizophrenia is viewed as a collection of types or related subgroups), dementia praecox would be considered as a "worst case scenario." We are not talking here of a splitting of psychological processes or anything of that nature. The pathology is organic (and from a mainstream medical standpoint, irreversible).

With this in mind, it is not surprising that Cayce recognized the necessity of a long duration of treatment in this particular case. In reading 271-5, he remarked:

> It [treatment] will be long (as time is counted by individuals), it will mean persistence, it will mean patience, it will mean keeping the mental balance in spiritual creative forces that are the builders for the body.

Although Cayce sometimes provided a specific time frame as part of his prognosis, in this case he did not. Perhaps this was linked to the duration of the illness. In other cases, he sometimes commented that early intervention could mean faster (and surer) results. This is consistent with the views of contemporary psychiatry. Early diagnosis and treatment of schizophrenia is associated with shorter duration of treatment and better outcome.

Naturally, in cases of long-standing pathology, it would be difficult for a companion to maintain a consistent treatment regimen. Frequently in such cases, the entranced Cayce would make a referral to the Still-Hildreth Osteopathic Sanatorium in Macon, Missouri. This remarkable institution was employing many of the natural methods of healing recommended in the readings. Doctor A. G. Hildreth, using records maintained at the Still-Hildreth Sanatorium, also emphasized the importance of early diagnosis and intervention by citing the following statistics:

RESULTS IN 840 CASES OF DEMENTIA PRAECOX
Admitted within first 6 months of illness
   263 patients. Recovered 179, or 68 percent.
Duration of illness 6 months to 1 year
   163 patients. Recovered 78, or 48 percent.
Duration of illness 1 to 2 years
   129 patients. Recovered 37, or 29 percent.
Duration of illness over 2 years
   285 patients. Recovered 57, or 20 percent.

When all cases of dementia praecox were considered as a group, a cure rate of 38 percent was reported. The dramatically improved prognosis produced by early intervention led Hildreth to proclaim, "It is our firm belief that if patients could be given osteopathic treatment at the onset of the condition in dementia praecox, the percentage of cures would be much greater: nearer one hundred percent than thirty-eight."

Some Key Points to Remember

In many respects, this chapter has laid the foundation for the chapters which follow. First, we encountered the concept of variability within schizophrenia. Variability is a bugaboo for medical research. Inconsistent research findings, lack of replication, and constantly changing diagnostic criteria result from variability. If schizophrenia is actually a group of related disorders, we need to define these groups and adjust our classification system accordingly.

It is important to recognize variability now at the beginning of our consideration of the Cayce material. The numerous case studies which we will examine acknowledge the various "types and natures" of schizophrenia.

We have taken the time to review the history of the diagnosis of schizophrenia. We have encountered the term dementia praecox. Dementia praecox referred to a relatively specific illness involving brain degeneration, long-term decline in functioning, and poor outcome. When psychiatry replaced it with schizophrenia, the strong biological emphasis was lost and has only recently been re-established. Apparently, Edgar Cayce recognized the inherent problems with the term schizophrenia. Perhaps he stuck with the older diagnosis because it was less ambiguous. When he gave readings for individuals presenting with psychotic symptoms without the characteristic brain degeneration of dementia praecox, he usually abstained from making a formal diagnosis. He would simply state the cause, the nature of the pathology, and a treatment plan to address it. There was so much variability in such cases, he wisely avoided labeling these people with an ambiguous and limiting diagnosis.

In the chapters which follow, we will be using the terms schizophrenia and dementia praecox interchangeably. This is the simplest way of translating the older terminology into its modern counterpart. However, it may be helpful to also keep in mind that schizophrenia may be comprised of various subgroups. Dementia praecox might more accurately translate into the more severe and degenerative forms of schizophrenia—schizophrenia with strong biological pathology.

Furthermore, dementia praecox itself probably included various subgroups. I don't want this complex point to be a stumbling block for readers unfamiliar with the intricacies of psychiatric classification. If you find this distinction confusing, simply think of dementia praecox as being the same as schizophrenia. If you desire a deeper understanding of this subject, you may wish to consult a more academic treatment of the topic (see the Appendix for a more scholarly book I wrote on the treatment of schizophrenia).

We have considered the case of a young man which Cayce diagnosed as suffering from a form of dementia praecox. We have noted the brain pathology and treatments recommended to correct it. The causative factor in this case was not as clearly defined as in most of the case studies which follow. Cayce simply called it a "prenatal" condition. Several readings were given and nonprofessional caregivers had considerable problems implementing the treatment recommendations. However, after several months of therapy, the mother reported noticeable improvement in her son's condition.

We have also been introduced to the concept of holism. Holism is the foundation of Cayce's approach and will be strongly emphasized in the chapters which follow.

2

The Genetic Connection

◆───────────────

STUDIES OF HEREDITY represent one of the most substantial areas of research in schizophrenia. The idea that genetics is somehow linked to craziness goes back many centuries and is part of the folklore of mental illness. In this chapter, we will encounter just such a notion—that insanity can be carried in the bloodline (or in this case, literally in the blood itself).

Before exploring this case study, let's take a few moments to briefly review the results of some modern studies of heredity in schizophrenia. The most impressive studies have focused on cases of identical twins. In the simplest possible terms, this research indicates that when one of the twins is stricken with schizophrenia, the other sibling has about a fifty percent chance of also suffering from the illness.

The obvious objection to such studies is that environment could have been a causative factor. Specifically, the family system in which the children were raised could have produced the abnormality. Ingenious researchers have overcome this objection by examining the records of twins separated at birth and raised in different family environments. The statistics held true. Identical twins raised in different environments showed a strong linkage when one of the pair developed schizophrenia. This research has become widely recognized as proving that there is a definite genetic factor at work in schizophrenia.

However, interpreting these results is a bit more difficult. How does one account for the fact that on average only fifty percent of the cases of identical twins became afflicted. Why not one hundred percent? Apparently, some other factors must be involved. A little later in this chapter we will take a look at a possible explanation of this phenomenon, a concept known as diathesis/stress. First, we will consider the case of a twenty-four-year-old man who received a warning from Edgar Cayce concerning a genetic factor which made him at risk for suffering from schizophrenia.

An Unheeded Warning

Mr. [282] was fascinated by the occult. He desired to learn about psychic matters and even to develop his own latent intuitive abilities. His wife and sisters were also interested in psychic phenomena. They were strongly supportive of his seeking a psychic reading from Edgar Cayce.

On June 10, 1930, the first in a series of nine readings was given for this young man. This reading stated that:

. . . there are disturbances, and these—unless corrected— must eventually cause distresses that would be much harder to combat with than at present. These have to do with the glands in the system . . .

This ominous warning was reiterated nine months later when a life reading indicated that "these tendencies are innate." A life reading is different from a medical reading in that it emphasizes psychological and spiritual (or soul) factors which influence us.

Note the choice of words used by Edgar Cayce. The expression "innate tendencies" is an important clue to understanding the types of genetic factors associated with schizophrenia. We will address this distinction a little later.

Apparently [282] and his family did not recognize the seriousness of the warning given in his initial reading. They were aware that there was a history of mental illness in their family heritage. They knew that an aunt on his father's side was confined to a mental institution.

However, [282] did not heed the suggestion to utilize the electrical appliance (the Wet Cell Battery) which was recommended. Eight years later in 1939, when Mr. [282] was suffering a schizophrenic breakdown, the entranced Cayce remarked: "The warnings were given—they were NOT heeded!"

The first symptoms of psychosis began in the early months of 1938. Correspondence from this period clearly indicates the nature and severity of the problem. Hugh Lynn Cayce, the eldest son of Edgar Cayce, wrote his father on March 15, 1938, cautioning Edgar of [282]'s behavior: "The situation with [282] here is peculiar. I am hoping to be of some help to him. He simply has a strange twist which borders on religious fanaticism." Ten days later, Hugh Lynn noted that [282] had apparently regained his mental equilibrium and "seems perfectly balanced."

On May 13, a friend noted: "[282] at the present moment is flopping around from one enthusiasm to another, not rooted in any one thing. I feel he has nothing stable nor of any permanent constructive value to contribute to the Association [for Research and Enlightenment]."

Following the first in a series of breakdowns, a letter from [282]'s wife dated July 3, 1938, informed Edgar Cayce that:

> ... Both doctors here suggest an institution but none of us want to take the responsibility on our shoulders, so an uncle suggested we send him to Germany where his mother ... has money and can take him to doctors and care for him, and, too, he would not be with strangers, and would not annoy friends of the family here.

Now let us look at a portion of a reading given for this man during the acute stage of his illness. Reading 282-8 was given on July 6, 1938, in response to a request from [282]'s wife.

> We find that from and through the highly sensitive and nervous conditions, owing to material as well as mental reactions, there are incoordinations between the impulses and the physical activities.
>
> These produce MENTAL reactions of an UNUNIFORM or of

an exaggerated nature within the mental and physical bodies.

If there would be brought anything near to normalcy, there must be not only a change of environment, a change of scenes, but a change of thought as well.

If there will be a great change wrought in the physical and in the environmental forces of the body, and under the new environs the low electrical forces [Wet Cell Appliance] applied for the creating of the better vibratory forces, with suggestive therapeutics—or mental suggestions for the body applied—these as we find would bring the normal forces and near to normal reactions through this body.

Note the similarities in the treatment plan for this young man and the case of [271] in Chapter One. First there was to be a change of environment. Electrotherapy combined with suggestive therapeutics could then alter the glandular imbalances which were affecting the nervous systems. A follow-up question sought clarification on the best possible environment for [282]:

Q. Would placing entity on a farm restore his balance?

A. Not as we find; unless there is an entire change of environs and outlook, as WELL as the application of those suggestive forces and the low electrical forces, to CLOSE as it were the centers through the system to the influences from without—which naturally produces a softening of the reaction between the impulses of the nerve forces themselves.

So just taking him to a rural area with clean air and natural surroundings were not sufficient to produce healing. The physical and mental therapies were necessary. Note the reference to closing "the centers through the system to the influences from without . . . " We will get more deeply into the concept of "centers" and "influences from without" in the second part of this book when we discuss transpersonal aspects of schizophrenia such as the kundalini energy and discarnate possession. At this time, I will only remind the reader that [282] had spent many years immersed in the occult. His intense metaphysical preoccupation may have led to an "opening of the centers" and certain psychotic symptoms.

I would also call your attention to the expression "softening of the reaction between the impulses of the nerve forces themselves." This appears to be describing the early stages of dementia, a condition explicitly associated with possession in several cases in the readings (see Chapter Twelve). Reading 282-8 went on to emphasize the importance of the spiritual aspects of treatment:

Of course, it is necessary that all that atmosphere of fear be eliminated. This may be done the better by not only the prayers of others, but the acting towards the entity and the working in the same manner that they pray!
Ye desire consistency, normalcy in the reactions of the body!
Then there must be THAT acted, and THAT lived by those seeking same for the body!

Mr. [282] received the treatments in Germany as specified in reading 282-8. Eventually he was able to return to the United States and resume a normal life. His mother remained in close contact with the A.R.E. (Association for Research and Enlightenment) over the years and occasionally mentioned her son in her letters. A few representative excerpts are included here to document the twenty years following [282]'s breakdown.

(9/23/46): "[282] is down in [. . .], Florida, to be near his family (ex-wife [301] and daughters [299] and [314]). He has a bank position."

(10/4/47): "[282] is doing well and is happy with his two daughters, especially [299] who is quite grown up."

(12/22/47): "[282] is in Florida, has a nice position at Purina's."

(3/19/55): "[282] writes contented letters, has his own bungalow and enjoys his daughters and grandchildren."

A letter from Mr. [282] to Hugh Lynn Cayce dated January 20, 1959 (over twenty years after his initial breakdown), concludes:

Through my mother I have heard that the Association continues to be active in many ways, so I am writing to let you know that while it has been quite impossible for me to participate in a way in which I would like to have done in the past, I have not forgotten the many benefits my family and I have received, and hope that circumstances will permit some degree of activity on my part in the near, as well as distant future.

The recovery of Mr. [282] was certainly not an easy accomplishment. It required several months of therapy and a couple of years of family support. Fortunately, the treatment was provided very early in the illness. The readings frequently linked early intervention and consistent application with positive results. I make this point because many of the persons who sought Edgar Cayce's help did not apply the recommendations provided in the readings. This will become quite apparent in the chapters which follow. Therefore this case is exemplary in certain respects.

While the treatments produced excellent results, there was additional concern expressed by family members who feared that they might also have inherited the tendency for insanity. Mrs. [457] was a sister who was experiencing considerable anxiety over this possibility. She felt that she was on the verge of a breakdown and sought a couple of readings from Cayce to clarify the hereditary aspect of her brother's and aunt's mental illness. The following excerpt was taken from reading 457-4 given on February 9, 1939:

Q. Can I inherit or pass on to my children the mental and physical disease of my aunt?
A. POSSIBLE; but very, VERY improbable—if there is kept a normal balance of the elements in the blood supply for replenishing all nerve energies of the system; which CAN be, may be tested by an analysis of the bloodstream for those hormones of the perfect coagulation and perfect balance between red blood and white blood supply.
Q. Can childbirth cause it?
A. Not in this body.
Q. Can I be in any way affected by it?
A. Only as the mental self dwells upon same and thus create a field, an attitude for such reactions as to cause a disturbance.
Q. Could overwork or any overstrain bring about this mental snap?
A. Only as such would bring deterioration to that supply as indicated, that must be kept in balance.
Q. Is it true that this mental weakness has been in the family for generations and comes up at intervals?

A. Where there is the lack of sufficient of the negative and positive plasm about each blood center, such is a weakness.

So this reading confirmed that the tendency for mental illness was a family trait which could manifest when conditions of imbalance were present. The tone of this and a subsequent reading was to minimize the genetic vulnerability and focus on how the condition could be prevented. The following selection from reading 457-5 is significant because it provides specific means of detecting and curtailing the hereditary factor:

One of the sexes is not more subject than the other. And the injection of new blood will soon change the whole situation—or in ONE generation, though it may skip and enter the next.

The condition is, as indicated there, the number of positive units about the center of the atomic force as related to procreation; and this—as is used in body-building when there is the age or the certain environs as to cause or produce a deteriorating or lack of activities in the procreation of the atoms for its re-creation—brings about a lack of those elements as we have indicated.

Hence the active forces that create those in body—structure of the natures which add to the nerve plasm, or the grey matter in same, would be the corrective measures; as may be had by the vibratory influence of Gold or Silver—dependent upon that found to be lacking in the blood plasm.

It would not be necessary that ANY have more than one such test, IF there is then ADDED, through such a vibratory means or manner, those hormones that would bring a normal balance for the cycle of procreative forces. Ready for questions.

Q. Should the blood test be made by any or all members of my family?

A. Only if there is the desire for procreation.

Q. Should tests be made at definite intervals?

A. As we have indicated, only once is necessary IF those proportions of the influences necessary are added to bring a normal balance.

Q. Could my brother [452] affect his wife or his children in any way? [he was thinking of getting married]

A. Should not—if there are the precautions, or if there are the activities such as to bring that balance necessary in the whole system. There's NO affectation!

Q. Is my brother [282]'s case anything similar? Has he inherited anything, or has he a similar blood condition?

A. Read what has been given respecting this in times past! The warnings were given—they were NOT heeded!

Q. What precautions should be taken in the case of [282]'s children?

A. These should not be affected. No precaution necessary here.

Q. In the women of the family, would menstrual troubles or childbirth cause it to develop?

A. Not necessarily.

Q. Was my aunt's mental case due to physical condition?

A. To this deterioration as has been indicated.

Q. Has [282] inherited anything from her, or has he a similar blood condition?

A. Read that which has been given as to the warnings here—this is much better than to approach from the mental attitude of this body, [457].

Q. Any further advice to this body?

A. Do not dwell upon such. Be sure there is at all times sufficient Vitamin B in the diet, as well as with the blood test if found deficient in the procreative plasm then add same through the vibratory forces of Gold [Wet Cell Battery with chloride of gold].

These excerpts are consistent with other readings which maintain that a heredity glandular deficiency is involved in some cases of schizophrenia. Apparently, this deficiency can be measured by analysis of a blood sample.

The readings seem to portray a diathesis/stress model of heredity in the family of [282]. Diathesis/stress refers to a widely held view of genetics in which genetic factors may not necessarily cause a particular disease. Rather, they may only predispose the individual to the condition. Other factors (such as stress) are required to "trigger" the genetic factor into action.

In the case of [282], this stressor may have been the mental imbalance produced by his extreme religious fervor. The readings state that some forms of dementia are produced in persons "strained by great religious fervor or excitement." Perhaps the "strange twist which borders on religious fanaticism" noted by Hugh Lynn Cayce was a factor in [282]'s breakdown. His sister, [457] was cautioned not to worry about inheriting the condition—her mental distress could "create a field, an attitude for such reactions as to cause a disturbance." Perhaps the mental and emotional stress of worrying could also serve as a trigger to activate the latent genetic factor.

The concept of diathesis/stress is supported by controlled studies of twins who are at risk for developing schizophrenia. This research leaves little doubt that heredity plays an important role in mental illnesses such as schizophrenia. Yet heredity cannot be the whole story. As mentioned previously, even in cases where one identical twin develops schizophrenia, the other sibling (with identical genetic material) has only about a fifty percent chance of suffering the illness. So some other factors must be interacting with the genetic vulnerability to produce the condition.

Another Case Study Involving a Genetic Factor

There are a couple of other cases in which the readings cited genetic factors in schizophrenia. For example, Mr. [5690] was twenty-seven years old and hospitalized in a state institution when reading 5690-1 discussed the genetic factors leading to schizophrenia (or as the readings preferred, dementia praecox):

> There are physical defects in the cerebrospinal nerve system. There are also the lacking of elements in the physical forces, as produced by conditions—some a lacking of elements in the physical forces, as produced by conditions—some a tendency in innate influences; not as wholly hereditary innate, as much as hereditary tendencies. Then, with the physical defects, these in their combination bring about that as has been called dementia praecox. This an inability of coordination between sympathetic, cerebrospinal [nervous systems], and the general physical body.

Thus the condition resulted from a combination of factors including heredity. The physical defects were spinal pressures, a subject that we shall examine at great length in later cases. The hereditary tendencies were triggered by a "lacking of elements" produced by the physical injury. So here we have both sides of the diathesis/stress model coming into play. A hereditary predisposition was triggered into action by a biological stressor (a glandular deficiency resulting from a physical injury).

Note that Cayce appears to be describing varying degrees of genetic probability. The genetic factor may be quite strong or "innate." Presumably, in such a case, the hereditary pattern would require little or no stressor to trigger it into action. Alternatively, a hereditary "tendency" would require a definite stressor to activate it.

The readings recommended that Mr. [5690] be sent to the Still-Hildreth Osteopathic Sanatorium to receive spinal adjustments and electrotherapy. The parents could not afford the treatments and the man apparently lived a long life but was never able to care for himself.

Some Key Points to Remember

Without doubt, heredity is a significant causative factor in many cases of schizophrenia. The research literature strongly supports such a conclusion. However, in certain cases, other factors are apparently involved in triggering the hereditary patterns into action. To help explain this complex topic, we have briefly discussed the concept as diathesis/stress.

In this chapter we have considered two cases of schizophrenia in which genetics played a major role. The case of [282] is a fascinating example of Edgar Cayce's psychic ability. He was apparently able to detect the defective genetic pattern, forecast the result if left untreated, and propose a preventative measure. When the warning went unheeded, he was able to provide helpful direction for treatment. The positive outcome in this case underscores the importance of early intervention.

The suggestions given to family members to avoid the hereditary problem could serve as a helpful preventative model. In other words, the same interventions used to treat schizophrenia may be helpful in avoiding it. Specifically, the use of electrotherapy with gold was recommended to counteract the genetic flaw.

Obviously, a genetic predisposition for schizophrenia can occur at conception. The joining of specific genetic material contained in sperm and egg influences the probability of suffering this devastating disorder. Our next chapter will examine other prenatal factors (such as birth trauma) which can also predispose the newborn to schizophrenia.

3

Birth Trauma

◆

FOR MANY DECADES several European countries have maintained detailed records of their citizens' health habits. It probably has something to do with the socialistic style of government prevalent among these people. Socialized medicine almost automatically becomes a government project. Inevitably, a bureaucracy develops. Bureaucracies feed on paper. Fortunately, the paper trail has been transmuted into valuable insights into the causes of mental illness. Specifically, the birth records of persons suffering from schizophrenia have helped to establish pregnancy and birth complications (PBCs) as significant factors in the development of this illness.

Initially, researchers become interested in the statistical correlations between PBCs and schizophrenia. While there are many caveats to this research, for our purposes we shall simply note that there is a well-established connection between birth trauma and schizophrenia. For example, a baby who experiences breach birth is slightly more likely to develop schizophrenia at some time during the lifespan than a baby delivered without this complication.

Now this does not mean that every birth complication results in schizophrenia or that all persons suffering from schizophrenia must have suffered difficult births. The linkage with PBCs is small, yet to the statistician and researcher it is significant. In other words, there is something going on here, we just don't know exactly what it is. There have been several explanations for the association of birth trauma to schizophrenia. The most obvious is that the brain is somehow injured during birth. Over the years this injury eventually manifests as psychosis. This interpretation of the data does make a great deal of sense, particularly considering the fact that recent brain-scan technology indicates that persons suffering from schizophrenia tend to have brain abnormalities (see Chapter One).

As with many areas of the schizophrenia research, the Cayce material clearly anticipated later findings. In regards to PBCs, the readings were decades ahead of modern research in identifying the linkage of birth trauma to schizophrenia. However the readings tend to take a different perspective on the nature of the physical injury in these cases. The readings most often cited spinal injury as the primary insult to the nervous systems. This injury could eventually affect brain functioning and produce the symptoms of schizophrenia.

In this chapter we will consider the association between birth trauma and schizophrenia. Remember that schizophrenia is probably a diverse disorder composed of various subgroups. From this perspective, birth trauma simply represents one among several of the causative factors which can lead to schizophrenia.

A Case of Breech Birth

Reading 5014-1 was given for an eleven-year-old child who was suffering considerable developmental delay. Physically, mentally, and socially he lagged behind his classmates at school. A poignant letter from his stepmother dated November 11, 1943, vividly describes his condition and the circumstances of his early development:

> I have just finished TIR [*There Is a River*] and wish to say feel truly humble and greatly privileged in writing to ask if you would use your heaven-sent gift in behalf of our 10½-year-old body (who is my husband's son but my stepson). The child was greatly neglected and underfed for the 5½ years he lived under his grandmother's supervision. In the several years I have had

him my husband and I have done all possible to build the child's health up and mature him but he remains very retarded physically and also in all mental endeavors and in mental and social adjustments. Each new doctor prescribes something different to stimulate the lad's vitality and resistance but always thus far without results. We should deeply appreciate his reading at the earliest possible time for he is away at a small private special school in Massachusetts due to his retarded general condition, he is unable to keep up in the public schools. The expense of private school is greater than we can afford . . . God has indeed called upon you for a very great task . . .

The list of questions submitted with the application for the reading further describes the child's problems by focusing on the major areas of concern.

(1) How can we better build up child's physical and nervous strength?

(2) How much thyroid a day necessary to correct thyroid inactivity?

(3) Also what will keep the hemoglobin up to normal?

(4) What will tend to improve his extremely subnormal concentration?

(5) Please suggest treatment for child's extreme lack of effort and utterly irresponsible attitude toward school work.

Would greatly appreciate it if all the above questions could be answered as this child is badly needing help.

Due to the thousands of requests which came pouring in as a result of an article publicizing his work in a nationally distributed magazine, Edgar Cayce could not provide a reading for the lad until April 8, 1944, five months after receiving the application. To provide as much help as possible to the increasing volume of suffering persons seeking his psychic information, Mr. Cayce changed his format for giving readings. He increased the number of readings given each day and included several short readings in each session. Consequently, the readings near the end of his life became shorter and more focused on the problem and cure in each case. The accelerated pace of his efforts were a primary cause of his death a few months later.

Reading 5014-1 is representative of one of these latter readings.

The timing of this reading near the end of Cayce's life and the lack of a follow-up check reading to provide additional suggestions play an important role in this child's development of schizophrenia, as we shall soon see. Because the reading is so concise, I will include it in its entirety.

Yes, we have the body here, [5014].

As we find, there are disturbances preventing the better normal development of the body. These suppressions are in the areas where reflexes to the various activities or impulses through the body find their reactions; that is, the incoordination between impulses received by suggestions activative along the sympathetic nervous system and the responses through the central nervous system. We find that these are the sources of the retardments, the inability of concentration, the inability to coordinate the body's reaction with others; for the body becomes confused with groups or crowds. Thus those reactions in which the body attempts to shield itself, to get away from or to be closer to those who have respect for or interest in the body itself (as he sees it).

These conditions began with the period of presentation. For this was a breech or foot, breech and foot presentation. This brought about pressures in the coccyx and sacral areas that have prevented the normal reactions through the pineal. Not that portion having to do with growth but the exterior portions or to the left side, where there are connections in the lumbar axis, 9th dorsal, the brachial center and the upper cervical center.

First we would give that there be begun the use of the very low electrical vibrations from the Wet Cell Appliance used as the Radio-Active Appliance is ordinarily used. Both attachment plates here, for this particular body, would be of nickel. Be sure to attach each time the same plate first to the body. Use the Appliance for thirty minutes each day, preferably as the body is ready to retire at night.

Keep the attachment plates very clean, polishing with the emery paper each time before applying and each time when taken off. Do disconnect the leads from the Appliance itself when not in use.

Every thirty days, recharge the Appliance.

Each day following the Appliance give the body a gentle but

thorough massage with an equal combination of Olive Oil (heated) and Tincture of Myrrh. Pour a small quantity into a saucer, dip the fingers into it and massage along the spinal area, from the 1st cervical to the 9th dorsal, including the coccyx end of the spine on each side, and then massage from the base of the spine on each side in a circular or rotary motion UPWARD to the 9th dorsal, then very thoroughly in the 9th dorsal.

Keep these up regularly. Even through the period of giving the massage, as well as the Appliance, let there be suggestions given to the body in that way not merely of speculation but as to positive activities of the body; planning, as it were, its activities for the next day. As an illustration: On the morrow, or in the morning there will be certain activities. This should be very thoroughly outlined, very consistently suggested.

Thus, we will find a change in the activities of the body, bringing the reflexes to the brain centers with the nervous system in the ganglia where there are the closer associations with the sympathetic and suggestive nerve forces of the body.

Ready for questions.

Q. Should he continue to take thyroid medicine, if so, how much and how often?

A. Not if these applications are given. About once a week it would be well to take internally one drop of Atomidine before breakfast for two days in succession. This should be Mondays and Tuesdays or Wednesdays and Thursdays. Then wait until the same period next week. Keep this up each week for about five weeks, then leave off. The activities that will be produced here will be to purify or cleanse the glandular system, allowing the activities of the body for all of the glands to be coordinated by this low form of vibration and the reflexes to the brain not merely through the Appliance but the suggestions that will be made and also the massages that will be given to the body.

Do that.

Q. Any advice regarding the diet?

A. Keep away from too much sweets or too much starches. Do keep good eliminations, for there will be a tendency for engorgements in the colon. These may be aided by massages occasionally, as kneading or giving the treatments to the colon to add in emptying it.

We are through with this reading.

This reading is explicit in describing the insult at birth which was the source of this child's condition. A breech birth put pressure on the lower portion of the spine. To understand the nature of this injury, we need to briefly review some key aspects of anatomy and physiology. The pressure cited in the reading affected the coordination between the central nervous system (CNS) and the autonomic nervous system (ANS). The CNS includes the brain and spinal cord. The ANS serves as a mediator between the CNS and vital body functions provided by visceral organs. The ANS is composed of two branches (the sympathetic and parasympathetic).

The sympathetic branch of the ANS (which Cayce noted in this reading) is particularly important in cases of spinal injury. The ganglia of the sympathetic system closely follow the spinal cord down from the brain on either side of the spinal column. Thus, the sympathetic nerves are very vulnerable to injury.

Furthermore, the ganglia of this system are "wired" together in such a fashion that they act "sympathetically." That is, when one ganglia is affected, others will typically become involved.

This was apparently the situation for this boy. An injury at birth put pressure on the lower portion of the spine. Over the years, this injury affected other portions of the sympathetic nervous system. This in turn produced a pathological reaction in the pineal gland (in the center of the brain). We will look more closely at this important gland in Chapter Nine. For now, it is only necessary to recognize that this gland is an important regulator of physical and mental growth and development. According to the readings, it functions in close conjunction with other key systems within the body including the sympathetic ganglia which we have been discussing.

In the case of [5014], the net result was abnormal physical, mental, and social development. The description of the causes of social withdrawal provided in reading 5014-1 were prophetic of the models developed by the researchers years later.

Mednick was one of the key European researchers whom I referred to earlier. He has made major contributions in linking PBCs to schizophrenia. He also studied the extensive physiological research that had been done in schizophrenia and noted the consistent patterns of ANS anomalies which were found. Using a learning theory approach, he interpreted these ANS abnormalities as crucial factors in the production of psychotic symptoms. He postulated that a hyperaroused ANS could lead to social withdrawal and mental aberrations as a defense mechanism. This could happen as a result of another important function of the ANS. In the process of carrying out CNS instructions to the body's organs, the ANS is a crucial link in the "fight or flight" fear response that occurs when we are exposed to a threatening situation. The ANS becomes activated in a pattern which signals the adrenals to produce adrenaline and the circulatory system to change its flow to organs requiring more blood. We may experience extreme fear or even panic in such situations as the body gets geared up for action.

Theoretically, a person whose ANS was hyperaroused could be put into this "fight or flight" mode with the least amount of environmental stimulation. Thus, the individual might seek to avoid social stimulation. As a consequence of social withdrawal, the person would eventually lose touch with reality and become increasingly delusional and psychotic.

This simplified explanation of Mednick's model provides a context for understanding reading 5014-1, when it stated: "for the body becomes confused with groups or crowds. Thus those reactions in which the body attempts to shield itself, to get away from or to be closer to those who have respect for or interest in the body itself (as he sees it)." The social withdrawal was serving as a primitive defense mechanism. His nervous systems were telling him that something was wrong "out there" and that he needed to protect himself by being alone. He felt safer when alone or with the small inner circle of family and friends. He desired less stimulation to his nervous systems and acted accordingly by social withdrawal.

And yet, this psychological explanation is only part of the larger picture. The physical pathology, especially as it related to the breakdown within the nervous systems was a primary cause of the physical and mental symptoms in this case. For example, the incoordination in the nervous systems was cited as the "the sources of the retardments, the inability of concentration." Apparently, the poor school performance cited by the child's stepmother resulted, in large measure, from the lack of coordination between the CNS and ANS.

The treatments recommended in this reading addressed this basic incoordination within the nervous systems. As with cases presented in previous chapters, electrotherapy was a key element in stimulating the nervous systems to cooperate. Likewise, the spinal massages were intended to promote nervous system coordination. Suggestive therapeutics was advised to program the mind of the child. Specific, positive suggestions were to be given during the treatments.

Many of the physical therapies recommended in the readings produce a noticeable alteration in consciousness. Anyone who has received a relaxing massage can attest to the trance-inducing effects of this treatment. Hypnotic suggestions given during such a trance are very potent and are an invaluable tool in the therapeutic process. This important technique will be noted again and again in the chapters which follow. As we have seen in earlier chapters, it was viewed in the readings as an effective means of addressing the lack of motivation and oppositional attitudes associated with schizophrenia.

The readings often recommended a medication named Atomidine for cases involving glandular dysfunction. It was said to be a gland purifier and stimulator. The reading for this child noted that it would assist the other physical therapies in bringing normalcy to the body.

The diet recommendations to keep away from too much sweets and starches is sensible. It has also been suggested that this child might have suffered from hypoglycemia. This syndrome has been linked to numerous conditions, including schizophrenia. The suggestion to maintain good eliminations is also sensible. Constipation is often a problem for persons suffering from major mental illness. The resulting toxicity could compromise the body's natural attempts at achieving equilibrium.

The outcome in this case is extremely important in establishing the link between birth trauma and schizophrenia. Relatives provided several follow-up reports which deserve close attention. A letter from the stepmother dated May 28, 1950 (about six years after the reading), states:

> [The] child was retarded in every way. Behavior was very erratic and abnormal. Personality lacked integration badly and in every way. Always that way from babyhood. Physicians could not diagnose. Just said child was abnormal and retarded with sympathetic nerve and thyroid abnormalities and very little coordination or correlation throughout. Treatment outlined by the reading was carried out continuously except for 2 months each summer and we expect to continue another several years. First year—little improvement. Second year, some improvement noticeable and third year definite improvement

noticeable. There is no technical name we know of for his condition. No doctor (and we took the boy to a number) gave it any specific name. Mr. Cayce calls it a condition of general retardment as result of an injury to coccyx [tailbone] and sacral area at birth. He is not 100% normal for his age as yet. In fact he appears and acts a full two years younger than his age, but the improvement is 1000%—not 100%. The abnormal behavior and abnormal traits and neurotic characteristics disappeared several years ago. His responses (physical and mental) are still lower than average, but more and more all the time does general integration of the boy approach nearer a normal personality. His span of concentration which was but a very few seconds at the time of his reading by Mr. Cayce is now greatly lengthened. He now can study or concentrate without a break for 30 to 40 minutes. He has been unable to do any of his school work. He now is able to do all of it (2 years behind grade) provided he is allowed somewhat more time than generally allotted to the average pupil. It is very difficult to give specific definite facts, for this condition has been an extremely erratic yet subtle thing. Without Mr. Cayce's reading this boy's life would have been unmistakably one of great tragedy. (Massachusetts General Hospital Clinic in Boston diagnosed him as a permanently retarded child.) But there is now every promise and evidence that with continued use of the treatment outlined by Mr. Cayce that he will ultimately be normal. We may continue his treatment another 2 or 3 or even 4 years. There has been a tremendous improvement in physical coordination, too . . .

The descriptions contained in this letter suggest the possibility of Attention Deficit Disorder. Inability to concentrate and stay focused on task is the primary symptom in this condition. The research findings on PBCs and schizophrenia noted the significant linkage of developmental problems involving poor concentration and a variety of learning deficits. In this respect, [5014] was quite typical in his developmental pattern.

About thirteen months later, the stepmother continued to note significant progress:

My son still gets his nightly Wet Cell treatment, and is COMING ALONG. He seems sixteen rather than eighteen but is working six days a week, 8 hours a day on a truck garden and in school is an advanced sophomore. Without Edgar Cayce's reading he would have been a far cry from that today!

Unfortunately, the young man's improvement halted. A letter from the stepmother dated May 10, 1956, stated:

> You will be sorry to hear [5014] had a severe mental break in January and was placed in one of the State hospitals. He was highly irrational and showed typical schizophrenic (so-called) symptoms and was diagnosed accordingly. One of the new drugs, Thorazine, brought him back to rationality in about 6 weeks' time—since then he has been in his usual normal state—though perhaps in a little slower than usual motion in all responses. The State has committed him for indefinite hospitalization. He is in what is considered the ward for the nearest normal behavior, and is doing certain duties in either dining room or kitchen, and soon to be given yard work. This is not his first aberration. He had one in January 1955 and one in January 1953, I think, but of only a few days' duration—both more in form of amnesia, and of course was discharged from Navy in September 1954 as psychologically and nervously unfit.

Apparently, the therapeutic progress had halted about five years before his schizophrenic breakdown. His stepmother noted:

> Thank you so for your very kind, dear letter [from Hugh Lynn Cayce]. We certainly greatly appreciate your loving thoughts and prayers. I cannot help but feel [5014] is karmically held, for he seemed to cease to absorb help about five years ago, and these occurrences have ensued since.

According to the father's oral report in July of 1960:

> [5014] is still in the State Hospital but is allowed to come home on occasional weekends. He is happy there; he has regular duties that are not too strenuous or taxing on him physically or mentally.

We are left to wonder about the course of the illness in this case had Edgar Cayce lived a few more years and been able to give check readings during [5014]'s adolescence. In retrospect and based upon similar cases, it is likely that subsequent readings would have recommended osteopathic adjustments to correct the pressures along the spine. Also, chloride of gold may have been included in the electrotherapy. The readings often stated that this metal could help regenerate the nervous system.

One can also speculate upon the effects of the years of treatment provided by the stepmother. Typically, cases of schizophrenia with poor premorbid adjustment (childhood problems) have an extremely poor prognosis. The readings tend to agree on this point. The earlier the injury, the more difficult it can be to make corrections. As the young man apparently responded in some degree to the antipsychotic medications and was able to adjust to an institutional setting, perhaps the effort was not wasted. Based on the medical prognosis in such cases, the outcome could certainly have been much worse.

Other Examples of Birth Trauma in Schizophrenia

We will look briefly at two other cases where the readings linked birth trauma to schizophrenia. Mr. [3997] was nineteen years old when he received a reading from Edgar Cayce. He was a patient at Bryce Hospital in Tuscaloosa, Alabama (a state mental institution). The source of his problems was traced to spinal pressures produced during gestation and presentation. Glandular dysfunction was noted (especially the pineal) in reading 3997-1:

> There was in the inception, and in presentation at the time of birth, that which produced a pressure on the 1st and 2nd cervicals, that has hindered the normal development of the nerve as especially has to do with the reactions of generation, or gentation in the body—the pineal gland. The pituitary gland has become enlarged from same. The pineal gland being formed, then in two conditions that produce engorgement in same. Near the indentation or subluxation as produced, brings in the lower portion of same, or in the branches of same that act with the lyden [Leydig] gland, that causing the expansion of same in this region. Hence there has been the continued repression to the body in its development, until—reaching that cycle when the development of the genitory [reproductive] gland and the activity of the lyden [Leydig] gland in the system

[puberty?]—has brought about such depression and activity to the action of the imagination, or the activity of the gray matter in nerve reaction, until dementia is the result.

The prognosis provided by Cayce was sobering:

. . . the whole of the gland system builded nominally, we would bring—in the third cycle—near normal reaction for this body. Then, unless corrections are made . . . the general breaking down of the gray portion of nerve tissue, nerve cell matter, in the body.

In certain respects, this case represents a "classic" example of schizophrenia. This young man began having psychotic symptoms during his late teen years and was put into a mental institution. According to his reading, he had suffered an injury at birth, which is also consistent with the research on PBCs mentioned earlier in this chapter. As with the previous case study, Cayce noted a problem with the glandular system with special emphasis on the pineal gland. As we shall see in the chapters which follow (and particularly the chapters addressing the transpersonal aspects of schizophrenia), the readings place great importance on the pineal gland as a key modulator of physical and mental development and coordination.

Reading 3997-1 advised osteopathic adjustments to relieve the pressures along the spine. Close personal care and attention were also emphasized. Cayce's prognosis of improvement in the third (seven-year) cycle suggests that this case would have required at least a couple of years of treatment (i.e., until he was at least twenty-one years old).

There is no follow-up correspondence in this file and we do not know if the young man received the treatments. It is unlikely that he did because these therapies would not have been looked upon favorably in such institutions.

Mrs. [4342] was also in a state hospital at the time of her reading. She had suffered a number of yearly breakdowns prior to reading 4342-1:

IN THE NERVE SYSTEM: In this we find the seat of the trouble. In times past, in the beginning, as it were, of this earth's existence, we find the seat of the trouble—not a prenatal or congenital condition, yet one produced at the birth of the individual . . . this has produced . . . distortion to impressions . . . the brain, with improper distortion—these elements, the gray, the white [nerve] tissue itself—sets in motion, and when these become unbalanced, or distorted, the reaction in the brain, and then the activities to those incentives of the physical forces in body become distorted also, and to another mind becomes unbalanced. In this body, the pressure as produced at birth was in the presenting of the body itself, in that known as breach birth, and the pressure was produced in the last lumbar, and the 2nd portion or structure of the sacral, and the sacral then producing a pressure to those of the genetory [reproductive] system brought about that enlargement in those centers about these organs in pelvis, that direct connect with the base of the brain in this gland situated there [pineal]. The thread of same, which traverses the system from brain to the end of the cerebrospinal cord proper. With the pressure created in this position in this body, with the gradual development of the body, we have then this condition becoming aggravated. In the passing years, we find, as the body developed to the womanhood, this incentive has remained, making or producing in its reaction that of the eccentric, high strung, overactivity in every exercise of a mental prodigy, as might be termed. In later years, there came an accident to the end of the spine (four years ago—sixteenth of September, four years ago) which was to the end of the coccyx [tailbone], that which excited, as it were, these centers in the sacral and the lower lumbar. These reactions, then, are produced through this reaction to the base of the brain—a fullness, or an enlargement, that produces first headaches, then nervous indigestion, then a racking, as it were, to the whole sympathetic system, and an unbalanced mental reaction.

This case presents a slight variation on the pattern of the two previous individuals. While the injury occurred at birth, putting pressure on the spine and affecting the pineal gland, it varied in that an additional injury occurred during adulthood (age unspecified) which exaggerated the condition.

As was typical of the state hospitals of that era (and probably still is, for that matter), the spinal adjustments were not considered appropriate treatments. Consequently, the recommendations in the reading were not followed.

This was unfortunate because Cayce's prognosis was quite favorable: "In six weeks the body should be perfectly normal." This woman may have been prone to violent behavior as the reading states that she had been given bromides as a sedative and was in restraints at the time of the reading.

Due to the cyclical nature of the breakdowns and violent tendencies, this woman might be diagnosed as schizoaffective or even bipolar disorder by current criteria. The problem of diagnostic classification pervades the subject of schizophrenia. The difficulty becomes even more problematic when the person in question died many years ago. So the question as to whether this is a case of "pure" schizophrenia or overlaps with one of the other psychotic diagnoses will have to remain unanswered. The important point is that treatment in such cases follows the same pattern, regardless of diagnosis.

Some Key Points to Remember

In this chapter, we have noted research findings linking pregnancy and birth complications (PBCs) with schizophrenia. Although we do not know with certainty what the causative link is, we have considered one prominent theory linking PBCs to autonomic nervous system (ANS) abnormalities. The Cayce readings acknowledge nervous system incoordination while also emphasizing glandular dysfunctions (particularly the pineal gland).

We have considered three cases of schizophrenia which the Cayce readings traced back to birth trauma. In contrast to research findings which tend to be dry and statistical in their acknowledgment of these factors, the Cayce readings are explicit and graphic in their descriptions of the trauma and the pathology which can result.

I want to reiterate one of the major themes of this book. Schizophrenia, as it is currently defined, is a diverse disorder consisting of various subgroups and caused by multiple factors. So, just as I noted that heredity is not the whole story, keep in mind that pregnancy and birth complications are also only one aspect of this complex illness. In our next chapter we will consider the birth process from another angle. We will discuss the mother's vulnerability to injury during pregnancy and birth.

4

Pregnancy Complications

◆

ALTHOUGH STATISTICS TELL us that schizophrenia occurs equally in males and females, gender differences have been noted. For example, men tend to have an earlier age of onset, a poorer premorbid history and less positive overall outcome. Women, on the other hand, tend to suffer the initial onset of symptoms somewhat later, have better premorbid social adjustment, and respond to treatment more positively. On average, women diagnosed as suffering from schizophrenia also tend to experience more depression and self-destructive behaviors than men.

The meaning of these findings is difficult to discern. Do they reflect a difference in the way boys and girls are raised—in other words, environmental differences? For instance, one can postulate that girls in our society tend to receive more extensive training in social skills. Therefore they would be expected to have better premorbid adjustment, later onset of symptoms (since they would have more social support), and better response to treatment than boys.

Naturally, one might also postulate biological factors which could account for gender differences. For example, the female hormone estrogen has been associated with a decrease in psychotic symptoms. Women experiencing schizophrenia often have psychotic exacerbations when estrogen is low (i.e., during premenstruation, post-partum, and at menopause). Furthermore, they tend to do better during pregnancy when estrogen levels are relatively high. Some researchers have gone so far as to propose that estrogen is a natural medicinal chemical—that it has anti-psychotic properties.

At this point in time we cannot determine with certainty how these gender differences relate to the big picture of schizophrenia. Because schizophrenia appears to be a diverse disorder with many complex aspects, we can only keep searching for more clues to solve this fascinating puzzle.

However, the case studies which follow may help us to understand some of the factors which can lead to gender differences in schizophrenia.

A Case of Childbirth Leading to Schizophrenia

Mrs. [2744] sought a reading from Edgar Cayce for a skin condition from which she was suffering. Subsequently, two readings were given for this twenty-five-year-old housewife. At the time, she was a relatively average young woman. The letters she wrote requesting help in treating her skin blemishes were extremely lucid and "normal."

A third reading was given fourteen years later when she was in an institution suffering from "insanity." The breakdown had been predicted by Edgar Cayce in the earlier readings. The readings noted pressures in the pelvic region which could be relieved by osteopathic adjustments.

Recommendations for treatment had not been followed and mental illness had resulted. Here is an excerpt from her first reading which clearly warned of trouble:

> . . . there are those conditions more of which the body should be warned, and precautions should be taken in time concerning conditions apparent with the body, than that which gives such distress at the present [skin blemishes]. While there are those conditions that bring unpleasantness for the body, these are more of the secondary nature . . . these are not

the greater conditions to be warned against . . . The age and the conditions are at that point where corrections need to be made . . . for these other existent conditions will only build that which later would bring detrimental effects to the body.

This ominous note was echoed fourteen years later in reading 2744-3 which was given on May 8, 1942. Mrs. [2744] was in a mental institution and could not be present for the reading. The conductor of the reading submitted prepared questions to determine the cause of her affliction. As was typical, Cayce was able to recall a previous case even when many years had elapsed and thousands of other readings had been given in the interim:

There are many changes in the general physical and mental forces since last we had same here.
Ready for questions.
Q. What caused the condition?
A. As we find, and as we have indicated for the body, there were and are pressures that exist from those happenings at the time of childbirth. This pressure upon the centers—the end of the spine and in the lumbar and sacral-ileum axis—has produced those tendencies for deterioration of nerve reflexes. These conditions, as we find, will NOT respond to purely medical or drug reaction. There is the NECESSITY of the causes being removed, or the sources, if there would be any permanent help to the body. Hence we find that if the body were changed from the present environs, gradually leaving off the sedatives and removing the pressures—which might be done in the osteopathic sanitarium at Macon, Missouri [Still-Hildreth Osteopathic Sanatorium], there might be responses sufficient to regenerate and build the body back to near normalcy. Thus the body might have the abilities to resume many—or most—of its responsibilities, and it become as a helpful association with the family; rather than there being a constant question in their minds as well as in the body itself. It is true that unless there is the ability to relieve this pressure soon, there may be the necessity to give the body the vibratory metals—or the metallic reaction from gold—to aid the system in responding, for the nerves to the plasm in nerve tissue itself, AND to prevent softening or deterioration to brain cells [dementia].

So the reading traced the problem back to pressures upon the nervous system produced during pregnancy many years before. The advice in the earlier readings had not been heeded and the corrections never made. The condition had progressed to the point that treatment at home was not a realistic option. As I stated in Chapter One, Cayce often referred such cases to the Still-Hildreth Osteopathic Sanatorium in Macon, Missouri. And as was typical in such cases he provided minimal treatment recommendations, trusting the osteopathic physicians at the institution to carry out an appropriate treatment regimen based upon their assessment techniques and therapeutic model:

Q. If removed to Macon, is there any special direction to those in charge?

A. The pressures as we have indicated will be found to be existent. There should be the consideration of the first information we gave [fourteen years ago], for the corrections were never made properly. And this present information combined with same would indicate the condition existent through the pelvic, the coccyx AND the sacral and lumbar areas especially; though, to be sure, in the present there are lesions also in the upper portion of the spine.

Care, prayer, AND the better surroundings, would make for much quicker response for this body.

Q. Approximately how long would it take to correct the pressures?

A. This depends entirely upon the response, you see, and as to how soon this would be begun.

There is no indication in the files as to whether this woman was taken to Still-Hildreth. Some cordial correspondence was exchanged between Edgar Cayce and Dr. F. M. Still of the Sanatorium in regards to this case.

Note the time span of about fourteen years between the initial physical insult and later onset of mental symptoms. This is consistent with the pattern of pathology in many other readings on schizophrenia. Childhood and adolescent spinal injuries may take a number of years to manifest in a major psychotic breakdown.

Two Other Cases of Pregnancy-Related Psychosis

Mrs. [3996] was in a state mental hospital when her reading was given on December 26, 1924. She was suffering from paranoia and hallucinations complicated by self-condemnation. Reading 3996-1 traced her problem back to pressures produced during pregnancy:

> IN THE NERVE SYSTEM: This, too, we find under distress, both from pressure in portions of body by physical condition, also the reaction as received through blood forces not eliminating properties brings pressure on centers that deviates the sensory system in such a manner that the expression as found in the body gives those hallucinations that become so detrimental to self and self's satisfactions. In the pelvic organs we find the physical condition causing distress on the body. This produced in times back, at the time when there was the condition of pregnancy, and the pressures as produced brought the pressure in the form of a lesion to the pituitary or pineal glands, and reacting through pituitary glands in brain centers.

The reading went on to suggest deep osteopathic manipulations to the pelvis and some medications (notably, chloride of gold). The prognosis was positive if the treatments were followed: "Do that [the treatments] and we will bring this body [3996] to its normal conditions." We do not know if the treatment recommendations were followed. Like many of the cases of major mental illness for which readings were sought, the staff at the mental institutions of that era were unfamiliar with such treatment and adamant that such forms of therapy not be used.

The connection between the pelvic organs and the endocrine glands at the base of the brain (pineal and pituitary) will be explored in the second portion of this book. As was noted in the cases in the last chapter addressing birth trauma, problems with these glands was a fairly common pattern in cases of schizophrenia. These glands are part of a physiospiritual connection which I have labeled the "pineal system." This relates to the "body/soul" connection, as we shall later see.

Our final example of the perils of pregnancy involves a thirty-year-old woman who was just beginning to experience serious mental symptoms as indicated in reading 1475-1:

Yes, we have the body here, [1475]. As we find, there is rather a serious complication of disturbances with this body.
However, if there are the proper precautions and the proper applications made—IF there is the ability to save the mental reactions—the physical may be brought to near to normal, as we find.

The mental and emotional disturbances were closely linked to the menstrual cycles. Today she might be viewed as suffering from PMS (premenstrual syndrome).

Hence those periods when the body becomes so overtaxed by the emotions, and those activities as produced at the periods—or before—upon the functioning of the organs of the body.
Hence as we have indicated, the first consideration is to save the SANITY of the body, or keep that coordination between the assimilating system and that in which the cerebrospinal AND the sympathetic [nervous systems] may KEEP coordination.

The problem was traced back to her pregnancies:

Q. What specifically has caused this condition?
A. As we find, the great strain upon the body in childbearing WITHOUT the proper consideration of even keeping an equal balance in the salts and elements of the body; thus depleting the circulation, taking from the system the influences necessary for proper glandular rebuilding; thus drawing upon the system to an extent as to cause deterioration rather than the ability to rejuvenate itself.

She was in a hospital at the time of the reading. Her husband, who was present for the reading, remarked immediately: "I feel the reading fits her case exactly. She had three children within three years and was very 'faddish' about her diet throughout the period—not careful at all about building herself up."
The reading made several therapeutic recommendations including osteopathic treatment, electrotherapy, and diet suggestions. There is no follow-up correspondence and it is unlikely that she received the treatments advised in her reading.

Some Key Points to Remember

We have discussed research findings indicating interesting gender differences in schizophrenia. While the case studies reviewed in this chapter do not present any definitive answers to solve the mystery of these differences, they do provide some clues.

First, as has been noted in some of the cases in previous chapters (and will be re-enforced in the chapters which follow), the readings often cited spinal injuries as a cause of schizophrenia. These injuries frequently affected the lower portion of the spine and the pelvic organs associated with these nerves. Consequently, the nervous systems could be thrown out of balance and glandular functioning could be compromised.

The brain does not exist in isolation. It is constantly dependent upon the rest of the body as a life support system. Abnormalities in the peripheral nervous systems and glands may eventually lead to psychosis or even deterioration of brain tissue (dementia).

In terms of gender differences related to age of onset of symptoms, one might suspect that some of the differences could be due to social activities traditionally associated with gender. For example, boys tend to be more physically active and vulnerable to spinal injuries during childhood and adolescence. Since such injuries may take years to manifest as mental symptoms, it would not be surprising that the initial schizophrenic breakdown would occur during the late teens and early twenties.

Traditionally, girls are more protected from such injuries until they enter the childbearing years. Consequently, any birthing injuries to the pelvic organs or the lower spine would have its effects at a slightly later period in the life span.

Such factors coupled with the well-established hormonal differences between the sexes could play a role in gender differences. If this is the case, it will be interesting to observe whether statistics from future generations reflect any change in onset of symptoms in schizophrenia due the increased athletic activity among girls during childhood and adolescence.

A more integrated view would consider these biological and environmental factors as part of a complex interaction of variables. For example, the problems associated with pregnancy might act as triggers in a diathesis/stress model of schizophrenia. In subsequent chapters, we will discuss other physiological abnormalities within the reproductive systems of persons suffering from schizophrenia.

In other words, a variety of sex-related, biological factors could be involved in the gender differences associated with schizophrenia. We will now consider some of these abnormalities in the pelvic structure of persons suffering from schizophrenia.

5

Pelvic Disorders

_____◆_____

PREGNANCY IS ONLY one of numerous factors which the readings
linked to pelvic disorders and pressures on the lower portion of the
spine. In this chapter we will review several cases of pelvic pathology resulting from a variety of causes.

A Case of Dementia Praecox Produced by "Pressures That Are Associated and Connected with Organs of the Pelvis"

Miss [3441] was thirty-two years old when her father requested a
reading on her mental condition. In a letter to Edgar Cayce he
stated:

> She was a normal child and in her teen age took a very ac-
> tive part in all her school activities, making good grades in her
> studies. She graduated from "Peabody College" here in Nash-
> ville in 3½ years by attending both the regular and summer
> schools, graduating in August 1932 in Home Economics. After

graduation she substituted for two years then in the fall of 1934 she got the position as head of the Economics Dept. of one of our County schools. After teaching about three years she began having trouble with her vision and numbness in her right side. She gave up teaching about two months before her school was out and was under the care of several of the best specialists in Nashville; they thought at first there was a tumor forming on her brain but could find none by "X Ray." She improved some and went back to teaching that fall and continued teaching for the next two years. Just before her school was out for the summer she became very nervous but finished the term. After a complete rest through the summer she began teaching the next fall but gave it up after one month. We then put her in the Vanderbilt Hospital for a complete checkup both physical and mental. The Doctors again tried to see about a tumor but found no trace of one. The Doctor on nervous troubles diagnosed her case as "Dementia Precox" (Is that correctly spelled?) and urged us to put her in an Institution. We put her in the "Central State Hospital" here near Nashville for about a year. A friend told us of an Osteopathic Hospital in Missouri [Still-Hildreth?] that she knew had made some remarkable cures. We took her up there, she stayed four months, it was so very expensive we could not keep her there longer although she seemed to improve some. We brought her home and had to put her back in the Central State Hospital. Some of the Doctors do not agree with the Dementia Precox [*sic*] diagnosis but held out that there is something pressing on some of the nerves that affect the brain. I have tried to give you some idea of the history of the case, in hopes it will be of some help to you. I don't know exactly how to express what I want to say but in plain words—what do you think caused her trouble? The most important question is what can be done to cure her if anything? We have spent about all we can afford but if there is any reasonable expense that would put her back in normal health we would try our best to do so.

The background in this case is typical of the schizophrenic pattern in certain respects and unique in others. Apparently, this young woman had a normal childhood and excelled in academic achievement. During her mid-twenties she began having multiple physical and mental symptoms.

As noted previously, research indicates that there are gender differences in schizophrenia. One of the differences is the age at which psychotic symptoms manifest. Whereas males tend to experience symptoms during the late teens and early twenties, females suffering from schizophrenia often experience their initial breakdowns during their mid-twenties to mid-thirties. So Miss [3441] was well within the typical age at which such breakdowns usually occur with women.

Her case is unique in the neurological nature of the initial symptoms (trouble with her vision and numbness on the right side). The single reading given for this woman is short and I will quote it in its entirety:

Yes, we have the body here, [3441].

As we find, there are disturbances and there are tendencies towards the destruction of the reflexes to brain centers. These are produced from pressures that are associated and connected with organs of the pelvis.

Hence there should be those corrections made and pressures removed where those subluxations exist in the coccyx, the lumbar also in the 10th and 11th dorsal areas, so that better connections will be established.

These done, with the care that may be had under quite a different environment from that indicated here, we would bring nearer normal conditions for this body.

In making administrations for helpful conditions, then, we would put the body under the care and direction of such as the Still-Hildreth Sanatorium, Macon, Missouri. These methods, with the low electrical forces that may be used in connection with the osteopathic corrections, and the change in the environment for the care and the personal attention that will be given, will also contribute to the better physical and mental conditions of this body.

Sure, dementia praecox is indicated, but it is from pressures—that will respond. It will take time, but be patient, be persistent.

Ready for questions.

Q. Do you refer to the Wet Cell Appliance?

A. No, we refer to the low electrical forces of the natures that those in charge here [at Still-Hildreth] would use themselves, which are similar but of a static nature.

Do that.
We are through with this reading.

This reading was quite specific in describing the cause as "pressures that are associated and connected with organs of the pelvis." It is not entirely clear whether these pelvic abnormalities were produced by pressures on the spinal nerves or vice versa. Perhaps it was a reciprocal relationship where one exacerbated the other. We will look at the subject of spinal injury in greater detail in the next chapter. For the moment, let's remain focused here on the pathology in the pelvic organs.

Note that while Cayce acknowledged the diagnosis of dementia praecox, he asserted that "it is from pressures—that will respond." In other words, the reading recognized multiple types of dementia praecox resulting from a variety of causes. In this particular case, the cause was pressures associated with the pelvic organs. This type of pathology, if treated early enough before too much brain deterioration, would respond favorably to treatment.

As was so often suggested in such cases, the referral was made to the Still-Hildreth Osteopathic Sanatorium in Macon, Missouri. The phrase "with the care that may be had under quite a different environment from that indicated here" refers to a change in environment from a state hospital situation to the "therapeutic milieu" offered at Still-Hildreth. From the physical side, osteopathic adjustments and electrotherapy were the major therapies recommended.

We do not know whether the parents took Cayce's advice and returned their daughter to Still-Hildreth for further treatment. The considerable expense associated with a high level of individual care was cited as an obstacle in several cases which Cayce referred to Still-Hildreth.

Surgery Recommended for Mrs. [2197]

In a similar case, Mrs. [2197] was undergoing a schizophrenic psychosis when she received a reading from Edgar Cayce. She was also in an "insane hospital" at the time. She was depressed, suicidal, and experiencing hallucinations. "Indentations" in the pelvic region were cited in reading 2197-1 as the primary causative factor:

There is in the physical [body] those obstructions to the indentations of the action of the nerve system that produces aberrations and hallucinations in the manifestations of the mental, and the physical becomes abased with these conditions ... The nerve systems in the physical we find that depression first caused in the lyden [Leydig] gland that pressed, or indentations made on the perineurial and the pineal nerve center connecting with the lyden [Leydig] gland. This then gives the hallucinations in the vibration to the brain center or through the cerebellum oblongata [medulla oblongata?], you see. In the impression as this receives, there comes those conditions of melancholia, of self-destructive forces, of aberrations of depression as received and hallucinations to all the functioning of the sensory organism, through which these nerve connections find manifestations with the pineal nerve in its course through the system.

The treatment prescribed in this case was surgery to remove the "glands in the pelvic organs." Cayce stated that with such an intervention this woman's mental status could be brought to normal functioning. It is unknown whether the treatment recommendation was followed.

Note the references to the lyden gland in this reading. This gland was also occasionally referred to as the Leydig gland in honor of the anatomist Franz Leydig, its discoverer. The significance of this organ is that Cayce identified it as the "seat of the soul." Abnormalities with this gland were often cited by Cayce in various forms of psychosis. It is unclear in this case whether the symptoms would fit modern criteria for schizophrenia or one of the other major psychoses (such as psychotic depression). Depression is a common feature in schizophrenia. It is sometimes difficult to make a differential diagnosis. I have included it here because the lyden gland was implicated in the pathology.

As we shall see in later chapters, this gland is a key component in the body/soul connection. In the readings, lyden dysfunction was often linked to schizophrenic-like symptoms with transpersonal features (Chapter Nine). In other words, the woman was probably "hearing voices" and having a difficult time relating to "reality" as we know it.

The recommendation for surgery in this case does certainly seem strange, coming from the man who has been cited as the father of the modern holistic medicine movement. Yet, it is representative of Cayce's flexibility. His advice was based on what he saw as best for each individual. In certain extreme cases, even surgery was deemed best.

A Referral to a Gynecologist

The case of Miss [886] is a further example of Cayce's flexibility in utilizing mainstream medical resources. This young woman was suffering a nervous breakdown and hallucinating. A reading was given which described "a lesion in the lacteal duct and that as coordinating with the organs of the pelvis." The reading recommended that she be taken for a "very thorough examination by a gynecologist, for there are conditions that need local attention, as well as . . . rest of the mental and physical body."

Although he generally avoided recommending strong medications, he was aware of the necessity of sedatives in acute cases. He advised, "As we find, the hypnotics—that are preferable to narcotics—should be used."

The specific nature of the gynecological treatment was not given. Correspondence from a friend noted:

The girl had a nervous breakdown and was in a terrible state. On receiving the reading the family took her to Dr. C. J. Andrews [a noted gynecologist] who treated her with immediate results. The girl soon returned to her job.

The correspondence went on to state that the woman continued her employment for many years until her death in 1969 (thirty-four years later).

Schizophrenia Linked to Pelvic Problems in Brother and Sister

Considering the acknowledged role of heredity in schizophrenia, the cases of [3475] and [3589] are quite notable. They were siblings (brother and sister) suffering from schizophrenia. The readings cited problems in the organs of the pelvis in both cases.

Ms. [3475] was twenty-two years old when her mother requested a reading. Her mother wrote:

She suffered a nervous breakdown, diagnosed as dementia praecox three years ago. She was confined to sanitariums and under various forms of treatment for two years, then recovered sufficiently to be at home for a year, only to crack up again last January when we were compelled to return her to a sanitarium. Her condition is pitiful. She shows no sign of improvement yet.

Her reading stated that her problem was caused by "adhesions related to the organs of the pelvis." She was referred to the Still-Hildreth Sanatorium for osteopathic gynecology treatment. The attending psychiatrist noted: "The condition is a well-established case of schizophrenia."

Her brother [3589] was also in a mental institution (Manhattan State Hospital) at the time of his reading. Cayce noted "tendencies for inflammation to the organs of the genital system" and pressures in the 1st, 2nd, 3rd cervicals, and the coccyx. The reading stated:

There are those disintegrations of the sources or channels through which impulses are carried to the centers in the body for control of a balanced mental activity of physical being.

Osteopathic treatments were also recommended for this young man with the stipulation that surgery might be required to correct the condition.

The readings for this pair were given near the end of Edgar Cayce's life. Consequently, no check readings were given and no follow-up correspondence was received.

A Case Involving a Childhood Spinal Injury

Although there are numerous other cases in the readings which link pelvic disorders to psychosis, I will close this chapter by discussing the condition of Ms. [4333]. Correspondence from her parents indicates that this young woman "was a college graduate making a good salary when she got sick." The single reading given for her traced her problem back to a pelvic disorder involving the glands of reproduction:

. . . overtaxation in the mental, with the physical in the state of taxation, the weakened condition then forms that pressure wherein incoordination occurs in the body . . . cell force broken, came when there was discharged from the system that of the genetive system that is of the reproductive nature, and that in this taxation, then, we find these glands of reproduction that of the first cause . . . These glands are about the genitory [reproductive] system, and especially are these in that activity when the ovarine form . . . cast off their effulgence in its discharge from the system [menstruation]. The pressure, then, on account of the fall the body had in the sixth (6th) year that injured the spinal center near the lower lumbar and the sacral, produces a pressure in the overtaxed condition that produces reflexes in the pineal gland. Then we have these occurrences of the hallucinations, or the inability for the body to function normal.

Note the interaction of factors involved in this case. Mental stress combined with a weakened physical condition produced an "inco-ordination" in the body. The physical condition was listed as a glandular problem in the reproductive system. However, the reading skips backward in time to the sixth year after birth to describe a spinal injury to the lower back. The resulting pressure created a glandular imbalance eventually affecting the reproductive tract and pineal gland.

Cayce's prognosis was basically positive yet contained a warning to not ignore the seriousness of the condition:

Do not allow this to go so far as to produce the softening or the reaction in the center in brain from which coordinating radiation is made [dementia praecox] . . . [with treatment] within three to four moons, there will be found the returning of the full equilibrium in this body.

The treatments recommended in this case were similar to the other cases which we have examined: osteopathic adjustments to relieve the spinal pressures, therapeutic milieu with a spiritual emphasis, and companion therapy. One treatment not commonly associated with such cases was a recommendation for hydrotherapy during the menstrual cycle. Each day during her menstrual period, the woman was to sit over an earthen or crock container which contained 1 gallon of boiling water with 20 drops of tincture of myrrh, 40 drops of fluid extract of tolu, and 1 aloe. She was to allow the fumes to enter the vagina. We do not know if the treatments were carried out or what the eventual outcome was in this case.

Some Key Points to Remember

In this chapter we have elaborated on the theme of pelvic disorders producing schizophrenia. The common thread in these cases was a progression from abnormalities in the pelvic organs (and particularly the reproductive glands) to eventual brain pathology. In several cases actual softening of brain tissue was mentioned, usually diagnosed by Cayce as dementia praecox.

Cayce often discussed a close relationship between the glands of the pelvic area and nervous system functioning. Apparently, these glands produce hormones or other substances which are important for maintaining a healthy nervous system. Hence, abnormalities in the pelvic organs was sometimes cited as a primary factor in cases of schizophrenia.

The last case which we considered is particularly significant since the cause was traced back to a childhood spinal injury. In the next chapter we will focus upon the role of various forms of spinal insult which the readings associated with certain forms of schizophrenia.

6

Spinal Injuries

---◆---

ON DECEMBER 6, 1938, Edgar Cayce was at the McAlpin Hotel in New York City preparing to give a lecture. David Kahn, a businessman and avid supporter, had begun his introduction of Cayce when his focus shifted to a man entering the auditorium. Kahn strayed from his prepared remarks to tell a remarkable story of a man who suffered a nervous breakdown and was incarcerated at Rockland State Hospital, an institution for the insane. Kahn spoke of a series of psychic readings given by Edgar Cayce for this man. The readings described the cause of the mental illness and recommended a unique treatment regimen to cure the condition. The authorities at the state hospital would not perform the therapies and were determined that the man should not leave the hospital. Through the persistence of friends and family, the hospital officials relented and the man was able to leave and get the treatments. Within a few months, he was perfectly sane.

As Kahn completed his impromptu story, the man rose from his seat and came forward to meet Cayce. In a soft, choked voice, he said, "Every word of this is true, and I came tonight to shake the hand of the man who gave me back my life." When the man and Mr. Cayce shook hands, there was hardly a dry eye in the hall. To provide confidentiality, this man was later assigned the number 1513. Prior to his breakdown, Mr. [1513] had led a relatively normal life. He had been a mail carrier for the postal service for many years. The readings given by Edgar Cayce traced the man's mental illness to his job. The seat of the problem was quite physical in nature. Reading 1513-1 stated that some years earlier he had slipped and fell on ice injuring his tailbone:

Yes, we have the body, [1513].

Now, while we find there is a better coordination between the mental and physical reactions in this body, unless there are other applications to keep this coordination, or to supply the activities to the nerve energies of the system, we find that with the realization that there is an improbability of being restored to active service the condition would become very much disturbed again.

For through pressures upon nerve energies in the coccyx area [tailbone] and the ileum plexus, as well as that pressure upon the lumbar axis, there has been a deflection of coordination between the sympathetic and the cerebrospinal nervous system.

Thus we find impulses for activities become very much exaggerated; while the activities of the hypnotic [medication] that has been administered and the sedatives have allayed the conditions and created rather a submissiveness in the impulses through added suggestions to the body, and the activities in which it has been engaged—the sorting of articles and the weaving in which it has been engaged has produced some better coordination.

But as we find, if there will be the administration of the elements that are the basic reaction of nerve impulse and plasm itself carried into the system in such a manner as to make for a revivifying of the energies through the creating in the glandular forces of the body the elements necessary for the replenishing of the impulses, these may be brought yet to an active service for the body in such measures that there may be a restoring of the mental forces and a better coordination.

This would necessitate also then the supervision of a sympathetic physician that would make adjustments in the coccyx and the lumbar centers; and the application through the low electrical vibratory forces that carry gold into the system—in the low electrical vibratory manner, that the activity may become such where the body mentally and physically may be not only active for itself but as a help for the surroundings—and not as a dread to the family and the connections thereof . . .

Q. What was the original cause, or what produced this condition?

A. A fall on the ice, injuring the coccyx end of the spine.

Q. What caused the original pains in head?

A. Reflexes from those injuries to the pressures made upon the pineal centers.

Note that the reading acknowledged the symptomatic relief which the sedatives and occupational therapy had produced. It also went on to suggest that unless the physical basis of the condition were corrected, that the man would relapse into a worse condition when he realized that he could not function normally and resume his vocational duties.

The recommended treatments were aimed at relieving pressures on the nervous system in the lower portion of the spine (the coccyx or tailbone). Also, the glands were to be stimulated by electrotherapy utilizing gold chloride to help the nervous system to revitalize itself. During these therapies, the practitioners were to give positive suggestions of a spiritual nature (suggestive therapeutics). Companion therapy was to be utilized (at least during the first few weeks out of the hospital or until his mental status was more stable).

Mr. [1513] was removed from the state hospital inasmuch as the authorities there would not cooperate with the treatment plan. After discharge from the institution, he was taken to Dr. Frank Dobbins, an osteopathic physician. On April 21, 1938, the doctor reported on the progress in this case:

. . . I have given Mr. [1513] some 14 treatments as per the reading and in my opinion the pressure should be relieved from the areas mentioned. He should have a check reading to find out what should be done next. It was unfortunate that he didn't have the battery as it was to have been used in conjunction with the treatments . . .

Apparently the corrections to the spine had been made but the electrotherapy was not provided at the time. The requested check reading was given on May 14, 1938. The reading confirmed that the pressures in the lower spine had been eliminated. However, occasional osteopathic treatments were recommended to assist the electrotherapy and prevent a relapse to the previous condition:

> As we find, in the present the disturbances HAVE been eliminated; that is, the corrections are made in the coccyx area.
> However, with the vibratory forces set up for enlivening of tissue [electrotherapy]—which is the reaction from the Gold Solution or vibrations of same in the system—it will require that there be occasionally the gentle manipulations and the stimulation of the ganglia especially in all areas of the brush end of the cerebrospinal system; to prevent same forming or producing clogging again in the system.

Consequently, the electrotherapy was provided as per Cayce's recommendations and the man's condition continued to improve. The outcome in this case study was excellent. Dr. Dobbins's follow-up medical report listed the man as being cured of insanity. No further readings were requested and apparently Mr. [1513] went on to live a normal life.

A Similar Case with a Different Ending

Perhaps we can gain some insight into Mr. [1513]'s fate had he not received the spinal adjustments and electrotherapy as recommended in his readings. Mrs. [3641] was thirty-eight years old when she received a reading from Edgar Cayce on January 29, 1944. She was in Milwaukee Sanitarium in Wisconsin receiving shock treatments to relieve her mental illness. She had experienced six hospitalizations during the previous twelve-year period. Reading 3641-1 traced her problem to an injury to the coccyx (tailbone) years earlier:

> In the physical force, there has existed from long ago, those disorders that have caused a disturbance in the body dealing with the activity of the cerebrospinal and sympathetic nerve system, as related to the activities of the body in its glandular functioning.

There was, or still is, a disturbance in the second and third coccyx segments that is the seat or source or beginning of the disorder . . .
Yes, even in the present, we find that these can be helped—if there will first be the osteopathic or neuropathic correction of the conditions that exist in the 1st and 2nd segments of coccyx. Raise coccyx and release that tension that exists there . . .
Q. What caused these pressures in the coccyx?
A. When about fourteen years old, the body set down too hard on the ice.

This reading stated that improvement could still be gained through osteopathic treatments and electrotherapy. There is no follow-up correspondence in this case and it is unlikely that the woman received the recommended treatments.

You may be wondering what is so special about the coccyx that it should play such a important role in certain cases of schizophrenia. Considering the importance which the readings attach to the coccyx, it might be helpful to look more closely at the anatomy of the coccyx region, especially regarding the nerves and plexus in that area.

The coccyx gets its name from being compared in shape to a cuckoo's beak. It is usually composed of four small bones at the base of the spine, in other words, the tailbone. Of particular relevance to the present discussion is the nerve plexus associated with this portion of the spine. The major cords of the sympathetic nervous system closely parallel the spine and are joined in front of the coccyx at the ganglion impar. It is at this extremely strategic connection of the sympathetic chain that the readings trace many physical and mental symptoms. Presumably, pressure at this point produces aberrant reflex nerve impulses upwards to the major plexus along the spine (and in certain cases to the brain itself).

Reading 577-1 emphasizes the strategic importance of the coccyx nerve plexus by stating: " . . . most any condition may arise from injury or swelling or plethora (as more of this here [to the coccyx]) than from most any portion of the body, unless in the head or brain itself." The reading stated that Mrs. [577] was suffering from "acute pains . . . in varied portions of the body; making a dizziness, a heaviness to the activity, insomnia, melancholia, the tendency for the desire to be away from others." The reading stated that she had injured herself when "she fell on a dance floor—years ago."

Obviously, not all spinal injuries which Cayce associated with schizophrenia involved falling on ice and hurting the tailbone. In a previous chapter, we noted that in certain cases of birth trauma, the upper portions of the spine (the cervicals or neck area) could become injured. Thus, the readings contain numerous examples of variations on the theme of spinal injury producing psychosis. However, there did seem to be a preponderance of problems with the lower areas of the spine—the coccyx (as we have just described), the sacrum and lumbar vertebrae.

The significance of this portion of the spine is in the nerve plexus which radiate out to the organs of the pelvis, especially the reproductive glands and the mysterious lyden gland. We have briefly discussed these connections in the previous chapter on pelvic disorders. The case studies which follow will continue to emphasize these important connections.

"Pressure in the Lumbar and Sacral Region"

The precise age of Mr. [5715] was not given when a request for a reading was received by Edgar Cayce—only that he was "in his 20s." His reading indicated that he was in the early stages of dementia praecox:

> . . . there are distresses caused in the coordination of the sympathetic and cerebrospinal nerve system, produced by pressure in the lumbar and sacral region, which prevents that proper reaction as should come with the activities of the pineal gland and the lyden [Leydig] gland, through the medulla oblongata to the brain . . . [provide treatment] before the pressure produces the softening of the brain tissue itself; until there is dementia in its reaction.

The cause of the pressure in the lower portion of the spine was not given. The prognosis was cautious: "Will the body respond, it should be brought to normal, should this be taken in time."

Osteopathic manipulations were advised to relieve the pressures along the spine along with electrotherapy with gold to assist the nervous systems. Interestingly, gold was also recommended to be taken orally. There are several cases within the readings on mental illness where such prescriptions were given. No reason for the double source of gold was given. A blood- and nerve-building diet was suggested to maintain the balance between potashes and iodines in the body.

As the young man occasionally became violent, Cayce recommended that he be put in a hospital where he could be administered sedatives (bromides) to protect himself and others. No follow-up information was provided by this man's family and we do not know the outcome in the case.

The association of the lower spinal pressures with the lyden and pineal glands is significant in this case. Cayce stated that these glands were the "seat of the soul" in the human body. Certain key nerve plexus along the spine were cited by Cayce as important to maintaining communication between these glands. Pressure on these plexus could result in a variety of problems, including mental and emotional symptoms. We will look more closely at the body-soul connection in Chapter Nine.

A Childhood Fall Injuring the Coccyx

A childhood fall was given as the cause of psychosis in the case of Ms. [2721]. She was eighteen years old and residing in a mental institution when her mother received a reading on her behalf from Edgar Cayce:

> We find that in the beginning, a pressure in the coccyx end of the spine, combined with a delayed activity in the glandular system as related to the menstrual flow, caused these nerve pressures—in the lumbar axis, in the 9th dorsal, and the pressures upon the adrenals that hinder the glands which control the emotional forces of the body as to the secondary or sensory system . . . There has not been the destruction entirely of the normal reflexes between the sensory and the sympathetic or imaginative system AND the central or cerebrospinal system [dementia praecox] . . .
>
> Q. What was the original cause of her condition?
>
> A. An injury to the coccyx from a fall when only about three and a half to four years old.

According to her mother, [2721] had a normal childhood and adolescence before her mental problems began in her late teens. The reading recommended that she be taken to Still-Hildreth Osteopathic Sanatorium for treatment. Spinal corrections and electrotherapy with gold was advised. Her mother followed the recommendation. Here is a clinical assessment given by the attending psychiatrist at Still-Hildreth:

> The patient presents a morbid detachment and inaccessibility. The attention is occupied with a practically impenetrable reverie of random phantasy. No satisfactory discussion of her experiences is obtainable and there is mainly absence of response to questions. Alert and understanding cooperation is lacking and the execution of simple requests often ignored. There is mute indifference or an occasional mumbled and indistinct remark which has no apparent connection with immediate realities. The level of consciousness is insufficient to maintain adequate awareness and all sensibilities are in a measure clouded. Emotional reactions are impoverished. Personal needs are neglected and soiling of clothing at times occurs. There are dully delusional interpretations. The problem represents a well-established dissociation of schizophrenic type.

The treatments provided at Still-Hildreth were apparently helpful as the second reading given for this young woman indicated improvement in her condition. Correspondence from Still-Hildreth also noted progress.

One of the interesting facets of this case is the combination of causative factors described by Cayce. Pressures upon the nerves along the lower spine interacted with glandular changes which occurred during puberty. This might be a common pattern in schizophrenia—childhood spinal injury affecting the glandular system during puberty resulting in psychosis during the late teenage years.

Although the exact circumstances of the childhood injury was not noted in this case, we will now focus on a case in which the cause was acknowledged.

A Bicycle Accident Derails a Promising Artistic Career

Mr. [3223] was thirty-one years old when he received a reading from Edgar Cayce. His mental problems had begun when he was about twenty-one years old. A letter from his sister fills in some background information about the course of his mental illness:

He became mentally troubled about ten years ago [age 21], shortly after he had an accident on his bicycle. He did bruise his head and body rather badly then, but doctors have not been able to find anything physically wrong with him—he sometimes complains of headaches. You can imagine what a great sorrow this has been to my poor mother and father, who have watched this happen and have been unable to help him. The doctors have pronounced him harmless and as far as they know helpless. It is such a terrible pity that he has to be so afflicted, for as I remember him before he changed he was a lovely, kind, talented young man. He attended . . . Institute of Art and planned to teach art and planned to teach fine arts here—we have even now many beautiful drawings that he made before he changed.

The reading for this man confirmed that a bicycle accident years before was the source of this mental illness:

Now, as we find, there are disturbances which prevent the normal reactions between the sympathetic and cerebrospinal nervous systems. The injury to the spine, in the coccyx area that happened some time ago has destroyed those connections and coordinating centers in two particular areas . . .
Q. Was this injury referred to a result of the bicycle accident years ago?
A. On the end of the spine and the lumbar center. This naturally caused the segment in the third cervical also to be destroyed.

Cayce gave an encouraging prognosis in this case:

We find that these conditions may be materially aided. For, in most other respects, the body is very good . . . These as we find should bring better conditions for this body . . . Beginning with the second series of these treatments we should find helpful forces for the body.

The recommended treatment plan was standard for such cases: osteopathic corrections of the spine, electrotherapy with gold, balanced diet, and some mild sedatives (Bromidia) if necessary.
The reading made a reference to him being harmless. However,

it went on to comment that if he responds to treatment, some violent behavior may manifest and precautions should be taken. This pattern is mentioned in several cases where the patient exhibits a preponderance of deficit symptoms (i.e., social withdrawal, mental deficits, emotional flatness, etc.) before treatment but may become more animated as therapy progresses. The readings usually regarded this as a transitory stage and a positive sign in the recovery process. In this particular instance, we do not know if the treatment recommendations were followed.

"A Mental Disorder"

We will consider one more case study involving spinal injury leading to mental illness. This case is slightly different from those cited thus far in this chapter due to the stage of the mental illness. Cayce said that although this young man, Mr. [2200], was experiencing some serious mental symptoms, he had not yet reached the level of deterioration denoted by dementia praecox. In other words, if this person were to be interviewed by a psychiatrist, he might not necessarily be diagnosed as suffering from schizophrenia.

Presumably, Edgar Cayce's psychic gift allowed him to see beyond the immediate mental symptoms. He seemed to be looking directly into the body's nervous systems. The pattern of pathology was clear to him. Unless effective treatments were provided, physical deterioration of the brain was inevitable.

In times back we find there was an accident to the body that produced a lesion in the coccyx . . . While lesions have resulted from same in the lower lumbar, in the lower dorsal, and with the combined conditions that have been applied, we find sympathetic lesions in the whole of the cervical region. This produces, through these pressures, those spasmodic conditions to the reaction between the sympathetic and the cerebrospinal system—which has been termed a mental disorder. The reaction is not mental, but a physical—that acts to, or on, the mental . . . These come through, then, as repressions in first the sympathetic nerve system, from the lower lumbar plexus to the sacrals and coccyx, then to those activities in the glands themselves that secrete for the functioning through the pineal, and making for an engorgement and an inactivity or an ungoverning of the supply of impulse, as well as blood supply to the brain itself proper. Not dementia praecox, nor even a softening of tissue. Unless these conditions are changed in the impulses to the nerve system this deterioration must eventually set in.

The mother attempted to provide the recommended treatments but it was just too much for her. To complicate matters, her husband was not supportive of her efforts. She could not afford to travel to the osteopath recommended by Cayce and recruited a local physician to provide the treatments. Apparently, the adjustments were not made correctly and she had to compromise on some of the other treatments as well. Yet she noted that her son had calmed down significantly and the treatment seemed beneficial. In the beginning she was afraid to take him to the treatments alone. As he improved, she felt more secure in transporting him.

As time went on, she began to wear down under the burden of caring for her son. Edgar Cayce recommended that she contact the Still-Hildreth Sanatorium and see if he could be taken there for treatment. There is no further correspondence in this file to indicate what the eventual outcome was in this case.

The Still-Hildreth Osteopathic Sanatorium

As has been noted in several of the cases discussed thus far, Edgar Cayce made frequent referrals to the Still-Hildreth Osteopathic Sanatorium in Macon, Missouri. This institution was founded in 1914 by a small group of osteopathic physicians dedicated to utilizing the principles of their profession in the treatment of mental illness.

The physical facility was stunning—one could say opulent. The attractive architecture, spacious grounds, social and recreational opportunities, and medical resources were exemplary. Naturally, the cost of treatment was also quite high, by the standards of the day.

This was a serious drawback to many of the patients who received referrals to Still-Hildreth from Edgar Cayce. Keep in mind that many of the readings were given during the Great Depression. Also realize that many of these persons sought Edgar Cayce's assistance after exhausting all conventional medical resources—and in most cases, after exhausting their bank accounts. And yet Cayce considered Still-Hildreth a step above other private facilities—and miles ahead of the state institutions of that era (which were little more than prisons for the insane).

There are several reasons why Cayce held Still-Hildreth in such high regard. The institution placed great emphasis on maintaining a therapeutic milieu—a healing environment. On various occasions, Cayce implicitly and explicitly stated that there was a strong sense of spirituality embodied in the management of the facility.

From a technical standpoint, Still-Hildreth employed many of the same principles and techniques consistently recommended in the readings. The osteopathic tradition advocated "cure by removal of cause." Naturally there was a strong emphasis on maintaining balance within the nervous system by spinal manipulation. Various adjunct therapies including hydrotherapy and diet were standard. They even utilized electrotherapeutic appliances similar to or even identical to those recommended by Cayce. In other words, one cannot imagine a more perfect situation in which to apply the therapeutic recommendations contained in the readings.

Furthermore, there seemed to be an excellent rapport between the chief administrators of the Sanatorium and Mr. Cayce. This is more than coincidence as illustrated in the correspondence which circulated between Still-Hildreth and Edgar Cayce over the years. Here is an excerpt from a letter dated May 16, 1935, from Edgar Cayce to A. G. Hildreth. Hildreth was one of the founders of the Sanatorium and the principal administrator of the facility:

> I appreciate your letter of the 8th more than I can tell you; I appreciate your giving me the background for your interest in a work of this nature. While the time was short that I spent with Dr. Still on his visit some years ago in Kentucky, the most of it was spent in talking over many things that had happened in the experience of each. Of course, you can realize that during the thirty-five years that I have been doing this work I have come in contact with physicians of almost every school. A great many have shown interest. More have said taboo. And quite a number have, after years, come back and said, "We have found it worthwhile." That the information in the readings has more often and more consistently suggested osteopathy than any other one character of treatment, of course, is one of the things that has caused many of the medical profession to question same. Why it has done this I do not know, but we have quite a number of osteopaths throughout the country who are very well acquainted with the results individuals have obtained, even when applying medicine and other local appli-

cations in connection with osteopathy. Osteopaths seem more open-minded and willing to cooperate with any school of treatment which may help the individual. Just as our friend Dr. Frank Dobbins of New York City said some weeks ago, "When I have forty-eight cases that come with the readings, and I follow the treatments suggested—even though some of them are not exactly as I have been trained to give them, and I see all forty-eight patients get the results as promised in the readings, then I have to believe something." Or as Dr. Gravett of Dayton, Ohio, said some years ago, "When I see seventy-five cases osteopathically correctly diagnosed through the readings, I know there's something to it."

Dr. Hildreth, I do hope that sometime we may have the opportunity to each view personally the other's field of activity. I would indeed deem it a privilege to be able to go through your institution. And if you are ever this way again, I do want you to stop in and see the amount of data we have on hand, and the reports we have had from people all over the country who have gotten results by carrying out their readings—most of whom we have never met personally . . . We have had quite a number of cases of dementia praecox, but never one thoroughly tested yet with the treatment suggested through the readings; because the ones we have had have been so closely allied with the medical profession that no cooperation could be obtained in following any other mode of treatment suggested. In a few cases we have seen people removed from insane institutions by some sympathetic physician administering some simple remedy outlined in the readings, but these have been very few—and have been scattered through the entire thirty-five years of experience with this work. So, it is indeed a wonderful thing that such an institution as yours exists. I'm sure Dr. A. T. Still was happy, is happy, to know that such an institution exists—for the good it has done and may do for suffering humanity . . .

Hildreth's cordial reply not only discusses the treatment of dementia praecox, but also the underlying resonance in beliefs between the two men. It may also be helpful to note that the mention of Dr. A. T. Still in both these letters refers to Andrew Taylor Still, the founder of osteopathy. Hildreth's remark about his parents being spiritualists ties in here. Spiritualism was a strong movement during the late nineteenth century. Adherents of this movement utilized trance channeling to gain information from discarnate sources. A. T. Still was an avowed spiritualist, as was Hildreth's parents. I think it not an exaggeration to say that osteopathy probably owes much to its founder's spiritualistic beliefs. At any rate, this no doubt accounts in part for Hildreth's openness to Cayce and his unorthodox source of information. Here is Hildreth's reply dated May 24, 1935:

Your highly appreciated letter and literature came. I have read with very much interest all you had to say. The facts are, Mr. Cayce, I have been raised in an atmosphere similar to that which you found in Dr. Still and as to belief and liberality relative to the type of work you are doing my mother and father were spiritualists for a great many years before I was born before there was much known about that phenomenon and they were steadfast in their attitude, even through all criticism and ridicule heaped upon their belief. I am very sure you are doing a splendid work, one that is of vast benefit to a great many people. Note what you say about Dr. Still's joy over the work at this institution. He always stated when the time came our profession could own buildings of our own and surround those people with the right kind of an atmosphere there was a great number of the mentally sick that could be cured osteopathically and this institution here was in line with his thought and his desire and his sons contacted this property before I did and they selected me, or said they would consider it if I would agree to take charge of it. This was a source of great pleasure to Dr. Still and while its establishment came so late in his life that he was never able to visit us at Macon, only thirty-two miles from Kirksville, yet he was vitally interested and frequently sent for me to talk over our work here and always expressed his delight over the fact we had this institution here where we could offer our services to humanity along the line of his discovery. There is no question in our minds not only that he enjoyed this institution while alive but he is equally interested in it now and happy over the results we are able to produce.

I note what you say about dementia praecox and relative to Miss [. . .]'s brother. We will be very glad if we can serve them. There is no way to know other than by trial what can be accomplished for him, but a trial is certainly worthwhile. We are deeply grateful to you for your attitude. We are grateful we can offer to those poor individuals whose lives if they must live to the end insane, which is worse than death, a chance to get well. Don't misunderstand me, I appreciate fully your good words and your interest in our type of work but over and above my own benefit and my profession's comes first the glory of helping some body get well who has been pronounced incurable.

I presume you are well acquainted with conditions relative to dementia praecox, or rather the fact there is no treatment for it so far as the old system is concerned; hence, if we can establish, as we are, a percentage of cures great enough to interest the reading public perhaps the time will come when the whole world can recognize that insanity may be cured through osteopathic treatment or some similar method. As to the attitude of the old school men [mainstream medical doctors] relative to our work and yours, it does not bother me any because I know it is based on prejudice. It is too bad the whole medical world could not extend their right hand to any and all avenues that offer more and better results in the cure of dementia praecox and in the cure of disease. Like yourself I would be happy if I could meet you and have a long talk and visit and I assure you should we travel east anytime again we will try and make that opportunity. We would be happy to have you visit Macon, see and know for yourself of our work and our results. It is very fine of you to take the time you do in writing me such interesting letters. By the way, I am well acquainted with Dr. Gravett of Dayton and consider him one of my real friends. The facts are I know a great many osteopaths throughout the length and breadth of the land and only hope I can return at least in part to you in a way that will help you personally for the good things you say and do for our profession. With good wishes, I am, Sincerely yours, A. G. Hildreth, D.O.

Dr. Hildreth's extensive experience in treating major mental illness using the osteopathic approach lends an added dimension to the psychic insights registered by Cayce. In an article published in 1929, Hildreth elaborated on the various causes of mental illness:

To what are nervous and mental breakdowns due? This cannot be answered in a single word. The one word which comes nearest is "strain"—physical strain, mental strain. Mental overwork, grief, worry, religious excitement, etc., physical overwork, injury to head or spine, exhaustion from hemorrhage, operations, childbirth, etc., acute and chronic infections, and diseases of metabolism are causes. Physiological crises, such as puberty and menopause, inheritance of nervous instability, toxins or poisons, whether taken as drugs, formed by bacteria, absorbed from sluggish bowels, or formed in the tissues and retained in the blood through failure of elimination—all these are possible factors in the production of mental disorders. Of these, heredity is just a predisposing cause. Nervous instability is all that is inherited. Probably every case is the cumulative result of a number of causes acting in concert.

Break into the circle of causes. Remove all that are removable. Leave the rest to nature. Thus assisted, she is usually able to "come back." Such is the philosophy of treatment at Still-Hildreth.

One could not hope for a more succinct description of the causes and treatment of mental illness as portrayed in the Cayce readings. Hildreth's account encompasses variability of causation, the role of heredity (i.e., diathesis/stress), cure by removal of causes, and healing by natural processes. It is understandable that the Cayce readings so frequently referred difficult cases to the Still-Hildreth Sanatorium.

Although Hildreth was referring to mental illness in general, it is not difficult to find examples in the osteopathic literature which focus more directly on the causes and treatment of schizophrenia. Dr. Fred Still, a grandson of A. T. Still and an osteopathic psychiatrist at Still-Hildreth Sanatorium, provides insight into the relationship between dementia praecox (or what we would call schizophrenia) and autonomic nervous system dysfunction:

My theory of dementia praecox is necessarily based upon an osteopathic concept of this disorder . . . the autonomic nervous system is fundamentally involved and the distorted mentality and accompanying physical phenomena are symptoms of this difficulty. The basic regulatory functions of the nervous system, designated as autonomic, with their intimately associated circulatory and endocrine control, when in disorder gradually have their unfavorable effect upon the higher centers and account for the profound biological changes in the absence of constant and definite cerebral pathology. Early in this illness there should always be a hopeful prognosis. Deterioration is usually a slow and irregular process and certain to advance only to the degree in which the autonomic stress is unrelieved. The very theory of osteopathy is based upon physical causes which have their influence largely through autonomic action. The same fundamental principle which applies to the treatment of other organic disorders applies also to disorders of the intellect. In my opinion no field more truly demonstrates the value of osteopathic care than dementia praecox.

But just how can a misaligned spinal vertebra or some other physical malfunction cause an impingement upon nerves of the autonomic nervous system? This has been a key question raised by the mainstream medical establishment who felt so strongly about this point that they recently took the chiropractic profession to court to address the issue (and the chiropractors won!).

The answer to this question will have to await further research and a more comprehensive understanding of how the nervous systems work. However we can get a glimpse into the intricacies of the anatomical structures and physiological processes which are involved in these patterns of pathology.

Edgar Cayce frequently made explicit assessments of the various types of pathology which could affect nerve functioning. He spoke of subluxations, lesions, impingements, and so forth. He even went so far as to describe the location and nature of the pathology. For example, he might speak of a lateral, circular, or bony lesion. At other times, he simply chose to describe the condition as a "pressure" upon some portion of the system. Irvin Korr, the outstanding physiologist who invested many years researching osteopathic concepts, discussed the role of pressure in the formation and maintenance of the osteopathic lesion.

Now lest you anticipate that I am going to talk about the old-fashioned "pinched nerves" and such, I am not. I am going to talk about much more subtle influences that exert profound effects on cord function and its communications. These foramina contain not only the nerves and roots and their sheaths, but also quantities of fat, connective tissue, periosteum, blood vessels and so forth. We now know that it takes very slight, localized pressure or mechanical deformation to disturb the excitability and conductivity of the neurons that happen to be passing through a foramen at the focus of the pressure or deformation . . . In this environment the neurons are subject to quite considerable mechanical and chemical influences of various kinds, compression and torsion and many others.

While this quote is perhaps a bit technical for most readers, it does at least indicate that these concepts have been investigated by reputable scientists and described in professional journals.

One of the unfortunate historical repercussions of the acceptance of the osteopathic profession by mainstream medicine has been a movement away from traditional osteopathic practices. Most states now recognize osteopaths on an equal level as traditional M.D.s in terms of licensing and practice. With this acceptance most osteopaths have adopted a more biochemical approach to practicing medicine. In other words, generally speaking, they do not provide the same services which Cayce so frequently recommended in the readings. Many contemporary osteopaths do not have the training and skills to provide the spinal adjustments which were the hallmark of the early osteopaths.

On the other hand, the chiropractic profession has largely filled the niche abandoned by the osteopaths. Interestingly enough, the early chiropractors were also treating mental illness in their sanitariums with similar techniques and equally remarkable therapeutic claims as the early osteopaths. Dr. W. H. Quigley, a staff member of the Clear View Chiropractic Sanitarium for twenty-one years and director for ten years, shares his experience by stating:

When I first joined the staff of Clear View Sanitarium in 1940, I held strongly to the view that mental disorders were primarily of emotional origin. I frequently saw agitated schizophrenics, dangerous to themselves and others, arrive at Clear View in straitjackets, completely out of contact with the world of reality. They were not responsive to words, care, or any type of ministration. However, after chiropractic adjustments a dramatic change occurred, in which the patient began to orient himself by asking questions as to who we were, where he was, what happened to him. Soon he was released from restraints, had freedom of the ward and was eventually released from the Sanitarium. At first I felt this represented those persons who will make spontaneous recovery with or without care. When this type of experience was observed in patients who had been under psychiatric hospitalization for years, the change was difficult to reconcile with a psychological rationale alone . . . These recoveries were not limited to schizophrenic types but also to psychotic depressions.

The incredible therapeutic results reported by Quigley and others paralleled those published by the physicians at Still-Hildreth (see the table in Chapter One). In other words, when cases of schizophrenia were diagnosed and treated within the first few months, a cure rate of about 65% to 70% was achieved. Even in chronic cases, a rate of about 35% to 40% was accomplished. This is truly remarkable when we consider here that they were talking about "cure"— not simply symptomatic relief as we aim for today. The difference being, they were seeking "cure by removal of cause."

If (as Edgar Cayce so often diagnosed) so many of these cases involved various types of spinal injury, one could presumably address the problem at its source instead of waiting until it manifested in brain pathology. Even in certain cases where the brain tissue deterioration had begun, the goal was to encourage the body to heal itself by correcting problems in the organs which act as a "support system," as it were, for the brain.

Even allowing for exaggeration in these therapeutic claims, one cannot ignore the possibility that such approaches could make a significant contribution in the treatment of schizophrenia. Furthermore, these approaches were almost entirely consistent with the perspective of cause and treatment recommended over the years in the Cayce readings. Considering that we do not presently know what causes schizophrenia and view the disorder as incurable, it would seem appropriate to view the claims of the early osteopaths and chiropractors with an open mind.

One naturally wonders why these institutions no longer exist and provide their unique services. The answer is simple—economics. As we noted earlier, the Still-Hildreth Sanatorium was extremely expensive to operate. The type of care provided was labor intensive and usually required a minimum of several months to produce results. Consequently, with the cost of treatment being high, maintaining a solvent and financially stable operation was a problem.

To make a long and dreary story short, most of these institutions were converted into nursing homes which were deemed a better financial investment. I am aware of no contemporary institutional settings which offer the comprehensive array of treatments which these facilities offered and the Cayce readings recommended. This regrettable loss is certainly understandable when one considers the biological breakthroughs which were occurring in psychiatry during this era (see Chapter One). With the advent of the anti-psychotic medications in the 1950s, labor-intensive approaches to the treatment of schizophrenia could not compete. It was widely believed that these drugs would be refined and developed to the point of curing mental illnesses such as schizophrenia. This has not happened. Ironically, the current economic costs of providing lifetime medical and social services to individuals suffering from schizophrenia probably vastly exceeds the costs that would be incurred in a treatment program such as was offered at the Still-Hildreth Osteopathic Sanatorium and the Clear View Chiropractic Sanitarium.

If the psychic readings of Edgar Cayce were at all accurate in noting spinal injuries as a primary cause of dementia praecox (schizophrenia), it is difficult to imagine the potential contribution of a medical system which included traditional osteopathic and chiropractic therapies as part of a comprehensive treatment model for schizophrenia. We are left to wonder about A. G. Hildreth's observation that:

> Osteopathy is curing a percentage never heard of by any other system in the treatment of dementia praecox [and] other types of psychoses ... If only every mother and father who has a son or daughter afflicted with dementia praecox, a so-called incurable mental condition, could know there is hope for a large majority of these young people!

Some Key Points to Remember

Spinal injury is one of the most frequently cited causes of schizophrenia in the Cayce readings. There are many variations on this theme as we noted in previous chapters where pregnancy and birth complications and pelvic disorders were discussed as the source of the illness in certain cases. In this chapter we expanded upon this theme by noting various spinal insults which can occur during childhood, adolescence, and adulthood.

Cayce was not alone in insisting upon the prevalence of spinal injuries in schizophrenia. The osteopathic and chiropractic professions of his time were also aware of these factors and were treating them in their institutions. They had even developed a relatively sophisticated model of nervous system functioning to account for the physiological patterns of pathology. Typically, the autonomic nervous system would become involved, eventually leading to deterioration in brain functioning.

The pattern of spinal injury which we noted most frequently in this chapter was to the lower spine. The injury would put pressure upon the nerves of the coccyx, sacral and lumbar regions. Consequently, the pelvic organs associated with these nerve plexus (and particularly the reproductive tract) would become affected. Cayce stated that the brain required hormonal secretions of these glands to maintain a normal functioning state.

The pineal gland was frequently mentioned as being affected by problems in the lower spine and reproductive tract. We will consider this aspect of spinal injury in Chapter Nine.

The readings also noted other patterns of spinal injury which could result in schizophrenia. As we shall see in the next chapter, the middle and upper areas of the spine are also directly responsible for maintaining a healthy brain. When the nerve plexus of these areas are affected, the brain can become toxic.

7

A Starved and Poisoned Brain

◆

AS WE HAVE just seen, the osteopathic view of schizophrenia during Cayce's era recognized that spinal lesions could affect mental health. Dr. A. G. Hildreth, to whom we were introduced in the last chapter, graduated among the first class of osteopaths to be trained by A. T. Still, the founder of osteopathy. Writing in 1929, Hildreth linked spinal lesions directly to a "starved and poisoned brain":

> Lesions predispose the body to infections and maintain them in a chronic state, with absorption of bacterial poisons. Lesions disturb the ductless glands, whose secretions may thus become toxic. A starved and poisoned brain cannot function well. So the mind breaks down under a strain that normally would not affect it.

In the case studies which follow we will be offered examples of both a "starved" and a "poisoned" brain. Before we review these cases, let's take a deeper look at the physiology associated with these patterns of pathology.

Irvin Korr, Ph.D., is more explicit, albeit technical, in his physiological description of the effects of spinal lesions on brain functioning:

> We know of course that the sympathetic innervation extends to the blood vessels supplying the brain and the central nervous system and can exert a profound influence on blood flow to these tissues. Ordinarily this is a negligible role because brain circulation is regulated largely through arterial blood pressure, but it is well established that under certain conditions, when the sympathetics are stimulated in a given area, for example the superior cervical ganglion, there is strong contractile activity in the vessels to the brain to the degree that cerebral ischemia may be produced . . . Beyond this neurovascular control is the fact that sympathetic innervation has a profound influence on cerebral function itself, even the highest intellective functions. The results in experimental animals have demonstrated, for example, that various interventions in the superior cervical ganglia can either impede or accelerate the rate of learning or forgetting of conditioned reflexes and profoundly modify brain-wave patterns. So we see that the sympathetics have influences which are not ascribable merely to regulation of smooth muscle or secretory activity.

In his more technical explanation, Korr is essentially saying the same thing as Hildreth. Various forms of insult to the sympathetic nervous system can result in abnormal brain functioning. Keep in mind that the sympathetic nervous system runs along on both sides of the spinal column. It is part of the autonomic nervous system which we have discussed in previous chapters.

The essential point here is that the brain is not an isolated organ which can function independently of the rest of the body. The brain requires continuous support from other systems to maintain itself. Without this support the brain can die within minutes. Hence, abnormalities in other systems of the body can affect the brain resulting in the symptoms of mental illness.

Examples of "Starved and Poisoned Brains"

Edgar Cayce provided a reading for Mr. [4097] on September 16,

1922. In this reading, Cayce described how the brain was being affected by abnormalities in cerebral blood flow. The metabolic wastes from the brain were not being disposed of properly. This led to a toxic brain resulting in dementia praecox:

> Throughout the blood forces and system we find the normal action of the forces as presented or shown in the system, yet the blood carries the reaction of nerve forces as acted upon it, especially through the circulation of the brain forces and of the action of the nerve centers governing the flow of the blood to this portion of the body. In the nerve center of head itself, the seat of the emotions and expressions as received or transmitted through the sensory system, we find the action of the brain itself to be that of dementia praecox—that is, the softening of the tissue used to present the reaction of impressions to the centers as distributed from the action of the sensory system in itself, action of the body itself. That is, impressions as received to this body act refractorily on the centers giving off the impressions received to this body, so that we have only a partial action of the brain to give the proper incentive to the movements of the other forces in the body; or the impossible forces present themselves through the action of other portions of the body. So that the expressions as given off from the body to proceed with its actions become hallucinations, as it were, to other minds and the expressions from this mind become of a demented force in the actions; yet to the mind itself it is rational. In its impressions to others it expresses the irrational.
>
> This, as we find, has been produced by the breaking of cell force itself in the blood supply, as we have given here, to the brain force itself. Though this may be removed by the stimulus of nerve tissue and sensations, by the use of forces within the system to remove the condition as shown or expressed in the brain action itself; by applying to the centers that give the supply of blood to the brain and that remove from the circulation the used forces, as given off by the flow of blood through the brain, that can absorb from the system those impurities that have been left and caused the hallucinations of the body at the present time.

"Extreme nervous tension" was cited by Cayce as the primary

cause in the chain reaction leading to this man's psychosis. The precise nature of the psychological stress was not given. The stress affected the sympathetic nerves along the upper portion of the spine (at the first cervical vertebra). These nerves help to regulate the blood flow through the brain. With this breakdown in the sympathetic nervous system, the metabolic wastes from the brain (which are normally removed by the blood circulation) were allowed to remain and poison the brain. As the reading put it, "impurities that have been left and caused the hallucinations of the body at the present time."

The association of psychotic hallucinations to disturbed flow of blood to the brain was noted in several cases in the readings. Just as the case of [4097] reflected the "poisoned" aspect of this condition, the case of [173] is an example of a "starved" brain.

Mr. [173] had been "mentally unbalanced" for three years prior to receiving a reading from Edgar Cayce. Reading 173-1 clearly linked his psychosis to abnormal patterns of blood circulation to the brain caused by spinal pressures:

This condition is the form of hallucination dementia, and is produced, as we see, by a physical condition existent in the physical structure that prevents the normal flow of all blood to the brain in all its parts, for, as we see, with a nerve structure debarred by pressure from normal action, we have the same corresponding reaction to the brain proper. With this reaction, the supplying nutriment as is necessary to keep normalcy in body is hindered, through the inability of [the] bloodstream to furnish the rebuilding forces to that portion of the brain proper as becomes affected by this subluxation [of the spine] . . . This subluxation, bringing this detrimental condition, brings . . . the gradual softening of this center in brain proper.

The treatments recommended in both these cases of brain pathology were aimed at normalizing circulatory patterns through the brain. Spinal adjustments played a central role in correcting the impinged nerves. Electrotherapy was advised in both cases. Gold was prescribed for Mr. [173].

In the case of Mr. [4097], hypnosis was advised to supplement the physical therapies. Cayce recommended that he go to Still-Hildreth for these treatments. As was common with many of the readings given in such cases, there is no follow-up correspondence to indicate whether the suggestions were followed.

A Different Pattern of Brain Toxicity

The case of Mr. [4186] presents a variation on the theme of toxicity and psychosis. Whereas the previous cases focused on a toxic brain starved or poisoned by poor circulation, reading 4186-1 describes a more systemic form of toxicity—"uremic poisoning":

> Yes, we have the body here. Now, the abnormal conditions as we find them in this body have to do principally with the nervous system. Now, these are the conditions as we find them in this body—[4186] we are speaking of. There has been within this body an accident to the physical body itself, that with the fear of the condition that will bring this body to the end of justice, if done to the body that which would be justice to the body, until the weight of this on the mind has affected the whole nervous system. The accident we see has impinged the centers about the 3rd lumbar, and the condition affecting the organs of the pelvis to some extent, so we have at times this condition as we have through the action of the kidneys, and they in their functioning leave certain elements in the system to be absorbed, causing the uremic poisoning in the system, and it shows mostly at present in the capillary circulation, with the reflection this gives to the nervous system. It brings with this fear [paranoia?], a hallucination that comes to this body, hence the outward appearance—the action of this individual as it gives towards other persons. The organs of the system themselves function normally for the condition existing. They affect only those at times, only those that at times show through their individual action, such as we have with loss of appetite, the inability of the body to correlate incidents or happenings, and the fear of detection comes to the self more than as is the impression is carried to the brain centers, and acts on the body. The body is near to becoming in a state of dementia, which if allowed to go on will mean the destruction of the physical brain action of the mental and moral forces of this body.

So we are looking at a different form of toxicity in this case.

Whereas before, only the brain was toxic (and even then only specific areas of the brain), in case [4186] the whole body was toxic. Naturally, the brain was affected.

An injury to the third lumbar (in the lower portion of the spine) was cited as the original cause of the problem. This region of the nervous system innervates certain visceral organs including the kidneys. The kidneys eliminate wastes from the body by excreting them in the urine. A breakdown in this system can make the body toxic. The medical term for this condition is uremia.

Note that there was also a mental factor in this case. Apparently the man had been worrying obsessively about being found out for some injustice he had committed. Cayce said that the "weight of this on the mind has affected the whole nervous system." Remember that the first case study that we reviewed in this chapter also involved a mental stressor. The readings were adamant in stating that "mind is the builder." Presumably, destructive mental patterns can lead to actual physical pathology in the body.

Interestingly, paranoid features were noted in both of these cases. Unfortunately, Cayce did not elaborate on this aspect of the condition.

I will cite one more example in which kidney dysfunction was linked to florid psychosis. This case is particularly interesting because it also involves a pelvic disorder (see Chapter Five). Reading 4787-1 states:

> . . . the kidneys and their attributes suffer the most . . . on account of the local conditions through the pelvic organs . . . the brain force impoverished and the hallucinations at times become apparent in the individual action. In times back we find there has been a lesion formed in and about the pelvic organs that allowed lacerations to the organs and this has gradually brought about the condition existing in the body at present, so to give the better condition to this body, we would first have the removal of that producing the hallucinations to the mental forces . . .

As was sometimes the case, this reading was given for a person many miles away in a hospital. No background information was provided before the reading except that the individual was in a serious condition. Apparently the person conducting reading 4787-1 was unaware of the psychotic symptoms in this case. When asked to clarify his observations about this woman's psychosis, Cayce responded with characteristic bluntness:

> Q. What do you mean by this body having hallucinations . . .
> A. We mean the body has hallucinations. Things appear that are not . . .

Naturally, the treatment recommendations in these two cases of toxemia focused on bringing the kidneys into proper functioning. Spinal adjustments, suggestive therapeutics, and some mild medications were prescribed. There is no follow-up correspondence in these cases and it is not known whether the treatment recommendations were implemented.

Research Linking Uremia to Schizophrenia

Continuing with the subject of uremic poisoning, it is important to note that there has been considerable research into the possible role of uremia in schizophrenia. As early as 1960, researchers had reported significant improvement in schizophrenic patients who underwent hemodialysis—a medical procedure used to assist the kidneys in cleansing the blood. Subsequently, at least eighteen studies also reported significant positive results with these treatments.

As with much of the research in schizophrenia, these results are clouded by lack of replication in certain follow-up studies. A primary problem in this particular area of research is the low number of experimental subjects treated in each study. Since schizophrenia is such a variable syndrome and probably consists of a group of related illnesses, one would expect variable results. This is particularly true in studies with low numbers of subjects. In other words, each team of researchers probably assembled a slightly (or greatly) differing collection of schizophrenic subgroups. If uremic poisoning accounts for only a small subgroup within schizophrenia, some study populations may have failed to include any of these subjects. Or the statistical analysis of results may have "watered down" any therapeutic effect if they had been included. In such a situation, one would then expect to get variable results. The only conclusive interpretation that can be gleaned from these studies is that uremic poisoning is not the only or primary cause of schizophrenia. The findings do not rule it out as one of many causes. It is therefore likely that within the syndrome of schizophrenia a small sample of individuals may be suffering from some degree of uremia. For those readers desiring a more personal perspective on the possible role of uremia in schizophrenia, Carol North, M.D., has written a book about her own struggle with the illness *(Welcome Silence: My Triumph over Schizophrenia)*. Medication provided some symptomatic relief, yet the episodes inevitably recurred. Eventually, hemodialysis was tried with excellent results. Her story is an excellent inside look at the life of a person suffering from chronic psychosis. Her story is even more fascinating since she went on to become a psychiatrist.

Some Key Points to Remember

One of the major themes which runs through most of the cases of schizophrenia in this book is that the characteristic brain abnormalities associated with this illness can have numerous sources. According to the Cayce readings, the brain is very dependent upon the body's systems to maintain itself in a healthy functional state. A breakdown in certain key systems can lead to mental symptoms and eventual brain deterioration which Cayce identified as dementia praecox. Some of the key systems in this respect are the glands, the peripheral nervous systems (especially the autonomic nervous system) and the circulatory systems.

This chapter has focused on problems with the blood supply. In each case, the blood supply failed to support the vital functions of the brain resulting in psychosis. The origin of the problem was often traced back to pressures upon some portion of the nervous system. Psychological factors were also involved in two of these cases. The end result was that the brain was either poisoned or starved, or both.

The "poisoned and starved brain" model of schizophrenia was prominent among the osteopathic physicians of several decades ago. We have skimmed the surface of this literature to illustrate this perspective.

Thus we are left with some tantalizing correlations. We find theoretical models of brain toxicity and clinical interventions based on these theories in the osteopathic tradition. According to the published reports of these professions, treatments similar to those advised in the Cayce readings produced remarkable results.

We find current medical research linking more widespread forms of toxicity (such as uremia) to schizophrenia. Although the research literature is confusing, the fact remains that some of the people who have undergone hemodialysis have also experienced dramatic relief from schizophrenia.

So what does this mean? Perhaps it simply means that schizophrenia, as it is currently defined, is a diverse disorder caused by a multitude of factors. The population of individuals who are diagnosed as suffering from schizophrenia may consist of numerous subgroups. Conceivably in certain cases, deterioration of brain functioning may result from abnormalities in other key systems of the body allowing the brain to become "poisoned and starved."

8

Stress
◆——

STRESS IS AN illusive concept. A situation that is stressful for one individual may be exciting and pleasurable to someone else. Even if we can agree upon what stress is, what is its relationship to schizophrenia?

Two case studies in the last chapter involved some degree of mental stress as a causative factor. "Extreme nervous tension" was the term used by Cayce in one instance.

We also encountered the concept of stress when we discussed the role of genetic factors in schizophrenia. In that context, stress served as a trigger which activated latent hereditary tendencies. The technical term for such interactions is diathesis/stress.

The diathesis/stress model postulates that each of us is endowed with a degree of vulnerability. Under suitable circumstances this vulnerability may express itself in an episode of schizophrenic illness. This vulnerability may result from a variety of factors such as genetics, traumas, specific diseases, pregnancy complications, physical injury, and so forth.

Although this model, in its original form, did not specify the exact physiological nature of vulnerability, recent versions of this approach are more specific. Notably, researchers Nuechterlein and Dawson view information-processing deficits, autonomic nervous system anomalies, and social competence (coping) limitations as the prime vulnerability factors. The value of this revised model is its potential for integrating empirical research on cognitive deficits, ANS abnormalities, and social stressors.

Note that in this expanded version of the diathesis/stress concept, the diathesis aspect includes more than genetic vulnerability. This is an important point which will be borne out in some of the case studies which we will presently examine. In the first case, a spinal injury served as an acquired vulnerability which was triggered by mental stress into a schizophrenic syndrome.

A Case of "Overstudy and Strain"

Mr. [5405] was twenty-two years old when he received a reading from Edgar Cayce. He was in a mental institution when his mother wrote to Cayce explaining her son's situation and providing background information leading up to his incarceration. Here are some excerpts from her letter dated March 25, 1944:

> He has been confined for about 3½ years due to a mental collapse . . . Four series of shock treatments have been administered, the first, heavy insulin, and the second, third and fourth electric. The last has just been completed, but he is still far from well mentally, and besides is extremely nervous and does not look too well physically. His case has been called "a very complicated one," and about ten psychiatrists have said that he will never recover but I don't believe them . . . Could he have received an injury at some time that has never come to light? . . . He was a delicate baby, had a number of small illnesses, also had several accidents and a few severe shocks. He has been well and comfortably brought up, has attended good private schools—except one, where he received quite a shock and from which he was removed. Part of his school life he lived at home and part of it he boarded in school. He finished military high, spent a half year in college and the other half in a West Point prep school when he broke down. He had been living at home for a year and a half when this illness overcame

him. He was a very good student until toward the end, then just average.

There are a couple of clues in this letter which can help us understand the causes of this young man's illness. Note that he had "several accidents and a few severe shocks" during childhood. He was attending school and living at home when he broke down. He had always been a good student "until toward the end, then just average." Here are some excerpts from reading 5405-1 in which Edgar Cayce ties all of these facts together into a story of this young man's breakdown:

In the present environs, and under the existent shadows, very little may be accomplished, for, those individuals in authority take little interest in even possibilities, where there have been, and are, evidences of this nature or character of dementia praecox which indicates the inability of the body to respond to suggestive forces, as indicated, or the reaction or reflexes from brain to the organs of sensory forces in their activity to the physical being. Yet, as we have so often indicated here, there are measures which might be taken where there may be brought, even under the disturbances, near to normal conditions for this body. This would require personal or individual application, not merely of the material or mechanical applications for resuscitating activity of nerve matter in brain center, but application of the spiritual attitude, prompted by love of fellow man.

. . . in the first periods of stress in study, and in an activity that brought a pressure upon the sympathetic nervous system which broke the connection with the reflexes in central portion of the brain, as to cause lapses, or loss of memory—inability to recall what had been.

The giving of sedatives, the giving of certain classes or characters of treatment, has destroyed the ability in the physical self to respond to kindness. For, as may be found in the experience of every human soul, the soul responds to all the fruits of the spirit of truth, when even the mind and body may not. But know that mind, in the material, is the builder. Thus, with the correct—or a direct—spiritual application of the tenets of truth—patience, long-suffering, gentleness, kindness, brotherly love—there may be help . . .

Note the remark, "this nature or character of dementia praecox." Cayce is again inferring that there are various forms of dementia praecox. In more contemporary terms, there are distinct subgroups of schizophrenia. Apparently, this particular form was deemed especially difficult to treat. Therefore, the psychiatrists had given up hope of achieving any degree of improvement.

Also note the reference to both a physical injury and mental stress (specifically "periods of stress in study") as causative factors in this case. Apparently the injury to the sympathetic nervous system (in the lower area along the spine) impaired his ability to remember. With this mental deficit, school work became extremely difficult. Under the strain of trying to overcome his impaired memory, he broke down under the "periods of stress." Medications and shock treatments which were given only complicated his condition by impairing his limited interpersonal skills. Cayce said that he was not even able to recognize and respond to kindness when it was offered. In a state mental institution during that era, such kindnesses were probably infrequent. So the first recommendation in his reading was to remove him from the "present environs" under the "existent shadows," as it were.

With the change in environment, the physical therapies were then to be given so as to address the problem of nervous system deterioration. Consequently, electrotherapy with gold and silver played a major role in the treatment plan:

> There is within the nerve centers that which, in the elements of material, contributes to the white and gray matter of the nervous system, and, as has been indicated, this may be in patience, in gentleness, rebuilded, even when destroyed much more than is indicated here. But with the use of these elements—silver and gold—to the body in such measures and manners as to supply those necessary influences to reestablish in the physical forces of the body those necessary channels along which impulses run, we may replenish, we may supply those forces, for even this body.

The Wet Cell Battery was to be utilized to deliver the vibrations from the gold and silver. Companion therapy was also an important ingredient in the treatment plan. With the assurance that a reliable caretaker would be provided, the administrators at the mental institution could be approached to secure the release of [5405]. A rural setting was mentioned as a good environment for applying the treatment plan. A primary qualification of the caretaker/companion was that this person be motivated by a desire for service:

> This would require, to be sure, that the body be released to a competent nurse, and the care would preferably be where there will be the ability for the entity to apply itself in some useful activity. The more out-of-doors, the better.

This can be accomplished, if there is first obtained such a caretaker for the body, and then obtain release through the channels through which entrance was first obtained to present institution . . .

> Q. Just where could these treatments be better followed?
> A. As has just been indicated, where there would be some individual who would care for this body, and in the attitude of doing it not for the money, but for love of the fellow man. Yes, there are many who will do so. These can be obtained, as we find, should there be the desiring to change to the farm for such, in Massachusetts.

To clarify the cause of this man's illness, a follow-up question was addressed to the entranced Cayce by his wife, Gertrude, who was conducting the session:

> Q. Do I understand that overstudy and strain was the cause of his condition?
> A. Overstudy and strain, and, as indicated, an injury in the lower portion of the lumbar axis, where the Gold is to be applied; and the massages should be daily, following the use of the Appliance.

As was so often the situation in the case studies which we have examined, there is no follow-up correspondence indicating the outcome. Perhaps the mother was unable to secure the release of her son from the institution. Maybe she didn't consider the recommendations suitable to her son's condition. She may have applied the suggestions and wrote to the A.R.E. reporting the results. Yet the letter may not have been duly received as documentation. This was an extremely difficult time in Edgar Cayce's life—only a few months before his death. A note by Gladys Davis (Cayce's secretary) which was included in this file does shed some light on the problem of maintaining lines of communication with persons receiving readings:

> On August 30, 1944, Edgar Cayce went with his wife, Gertrude, to Roanoke, Virginia, to try to follow advice in his own reading to get his health back. He died on January 3, 1945. It is possible that the mother of [5405] wrote us following receipt of the reading for her son and it was lost in the deluge of requests coming in for appointments which we were unable to make. We still had appointments for readings two years in advance when Mr. Cayce died.
>
> In any case, we have no record of hearing from her again, so we don't know whether or not the attempt was made to carry out the suggestions in the reading. In 1949 we wrote a letter addressed to the mother of [5405] hoping to get a report. It was returned marked DECEASED.

Mind the Destroyer

Mental stress was also cited as a cause by Edgar Cayce when the mother of [5228] sought a reading to explain her son's nervous breakdown. She stated that her son suffered his initial nervous breakdown while he was in high school. At the time of the reading, her son was thirty-one years old. The attending physician in his case diagnosed his condition as the "Hebephrenic form of Dementia-Praecox, mutism type." In his mother's words, "He doesn't speak at all and he doesn't act normal in some of his actions . . . "

Hebephrenic was one of the subgroups of dementia praecox recognized the Dr. Kraepelin (the "father of modern psychiatry"). The current diagnostic label for this disorder is "schizophrenia—disorganized type." Symptoms commonly associated with this subgroup of schizophrenia (as listed in the psychiatric diagnostic manual) include "grimaces, mannerisms, hypochondriacal complaints, extreme social withdrawal, and other oddities of behavior."

In this particular case, Cayce stated that the physical deterioration of nerve tissue had not yet reached the stage of dementia praecox. However, this extreme degree of pathology was imminent if the condition continued to be neglected:

> Yes, as we find, here are those conditions which if neglected will lead to such poor reflexes from brain to activities of the inferior muscles of the locomotories as to bring about demen-

tia praecox, or such softening of reflexes as for there to be little effect of the gray matter impulse indicated in thought, or activity, either voluntary or involuntary.

Such violent reactions have existed until they brought that dissociation or short-circuit in the areas between the cerebrospinal and sympathetic nervous systems, both in those areas in lumbar axis and in the brachial centers, here, or a violent nervous breakdown by overtaxing and more from worry about those things which were "not too good to think about."

These, as we find, will be aided the more if there will be the use of the Wet Cell Appliance carrying Chloride of Gold Sodium vibratorially to the 9th dorsal and also lumbar axis . . . These should be followed by a massage with Olive Oil and Tincture of Myrrh. This would be given neuropathically, at least every other day, while the vibrations from the Appliance should be taken daily.

One can only wonder just what the focus of the obsessive worrying was about. Sexual repressions? Some skeletons in the family closet? With our current recognition of the high prevalence of childhood abuse, one can certainly imagine numerous causes for such incessant worrying.

The Cayce material was decades ahead of modern theory and research linking mental and physical processes. Commonly referred to as the "mind/body" connection, this view recognizes the inherent interaction of thoughts, ideas, beliefs, and attitudes with basic biological systems within the human body. Cayce explicitly stated that destructive attitudes, particularly ones that are self-condemning or self-accusing could lead to functional and even organic pathology.

Another case illustrating the mind/body connection may be helpful here. Although Mr. [5380] was not suffering from schizophrenia, the psychosomatic dynamics in his case are similar to our present case study. To help us focus on the destructive power of the mind, consider this excerpt from reading 5380-1 describing a "deterioration of mental processes and their effect upon organs of the body."

In giving an interpretation of the disturbance as we find here, the mental attitude has as much to do with the physical reactions as illnesses in the body. For as we find, in the physical or purely pathological little disturbs the body, save sympathetically, but in the mental attitude there is so much of the making for the degrading of self that self-destruction becomes a part of the reaction, but it is wholly mental. And thus the nerve forces for the body, this body as any body, any individual, who makes destructive thought in the body, condemning self for this or that, will bring, unless there are proper reactions, dissociation or lack of coordination between sympathetic and cerebrospinal [nervous] system, and it may develop any condition which may be purely physical by deterioration of mental processes and their effect upon organs of the body.

Just as the readings often remarked that "mind is the builder," the reverse proposition may also hold true. Mind can become the destroyer, when it is allowed to program the body's organs with destructive information. In a sense, this destructive pattern also constitutes the reverse application of suggestive therapeutics. However, instead of the mind programming the body with healthy suggestions, the opposite effect is created. Thus, the mental stress of worrying or condemning self can lead to serious pathology as we have noted in the case studies we have reviewed thus far in this chapter.

From a therapeutic standpoint, the recommendations given for [5228] were similar to other cases of schizophrenia. Electrotherapy with gold solution was the central focus of treatment. A spinal massage was to follow the electrotherapy. Cayce stated that the massage would assist the body in assimilating the vibratory gold while also stimulating the nerve plexus along the spine. He compared it to "unclogging" a plumbing pipe that had become stopped up.

From the follow-up correspondence we know that most of the recommendations were not followed. The battery was not ordered. The mother took her son to a local chiropractor who insisted that another electrical appliance which he promoted would do better. The doctor also ignored Cayce's advice to pay particular attention to the brachial and lumbar areas. He preferred to focus his attention upon the upper areas of the spine.

This was a common practice among the chiropractors of that era. It was referred to as the "hole in one" approach to correcting the spine. In short, the idea was to treat only the cervical vertebrae (the uppermost area of the spine, the neck). It was thought that if this area were correct, the rest of the spine would automatically adjust itself. Fortunately, modern chiropractic has evolved in its theory and practice to recognize the importance of treating the whole spine.

Thus, the recommendations in the reading were only partially followed. However, in a verbal report to Gladys Davis (December 12, 1944) the mother reported that her son had "greatly improved." Being a student of metaphysics, the mother was somewhat disappointed that the reading did not go into any possible karmic aspects of the case (we will consider this aspect of schizophrenia in Chapter Eleven). There is insufficient information in this file to determine the long-range outcome of this case.

Stressful Life Events

Although we can only wonder about the source of [5228]'s mental stress, the case of Ms. [386] presents us with innumerable specific causes which may have led to her illness. A letter from her father dated August 5, 1933, delineates some of the stressful life events in her childhood. This correspondence also clearly documents the anguish suffered by the parents as their twenty-year old daughter entered the early stages of a schizophrenic breakdown:

> I'm writing you about my daughter [386] who has hardly been real well since she was a baby, having had scarlet fever, diphtheria, adenoid operation, sinus trouble, etc., all of which has made her timid and sensitive and melancholy. Within the last week she at times has had hallucinations. [Her aunt] has been here with us and will enclose a letter with this. The doctor here at . . . Hospital has gone over her for about a week and finds nothing physically wrong but seems to think it is rather mental. I would appreciate it if you would give me a reading on her, for from what you have done for others I feel sure you can find the seat of her trouble and that which is necessary to correct same.

The enclosed letter from her aunt further described the background of the case:

> [My] brother and wife sent for me, feeling I might be of some help to them and [386] in her pitiful condition. I say pitiful, for to me a sick mind is the most pitiful of all afflictions. During the past week she has been under the observation of the best

doctor here, making all sorts of tests, etc., and his report was he could find nothing wrong with her but her mind [diagnosed dementia praecox], saying she must not be left alone to brood ... As I told her parents there is bound to be a cause, and until that is removed or treated she is not going to get any better, and there is only one way to get the absolute truth and facts and that is through you. So they are writing you now. She is so despondent and has delusions only at times ... I know the first readings are always thorough and definite, but please let one question be (unless given without question) where is best for her to go for a change and what best could or should she do to employ her mind. Her eyes are weak and she can use them little at a time. She has sinus trouble, hayfever. Has had two operations first when a child for adenoids and tonsils, which she says she has never gotten over, the other a lump in one breast, all without a general anesthetic, which I think has just shattered her nervous system ...

A subsequent letter from the father further describes the family's anguish and the attempts at finding help among the medical establishment:

As you know [before she came to you], we had [386] go through the Vanderbilt Medical Hospital where the very best medical aid is at hand and after a week or ten days examinations by the best doctors [including Dr. Morgan], they could find nothing wrong with her by every test. As I told you here recently we had Dr. Harris of this city, whom Mayo Brothers of Rochester, Minnesota, says is one of the best in the U.S. on mental diseases, go over her and he said very frankly it was dementia praecox and gave us very little encouragement or hope ... from what we have read and what Dr. Harris tells us, I fear she will not improve but will gradually grow worse ...

A series of three readings were provided for this young woman. Reading 386-1, which was given on August 9, 1933, traced her problems back to a period between her eighth to twelfth years when a series of shocks to her nervous system produced "physical suppression of the active forces of the mental body." This reading is so rich in physiological, psychological, and therapeutic information, I am including it here in its entirety for the benefit of those readers desiring a deeper understanding of Cayce's approach to this complex case:

Yes, we have the body here, [386].

Now, as we find, there are conditions that disturb the better equilibrium of the body-mental; and these have their incipiency—or foundations—in the mental or imaginative forces of the body, through PHYSICAL suppression of the active forces in the mental body—that is creative in its activity.

These, then, are the conditions as we find them with this body, [386], we are speaking of:

In the BLOOD SUPPLY we find a condition that is—while it may not be said to be abnormal, it is UNNORMAL for a developing or an active force in a body of such PHYSICAL abilities.

For, while there is not a great unbalancing in the white and red blood, the effluvia and fluor in the hemoglobin does not make for those activities that carry to the impulses in the nerve forces that which creates a balance in the responsive or reactory forces of a normal body.

A great deal of this has come through suppression to the PHYSICAL body, until it has made for an inability of the body to respond to its own self's reactions for that the body WOULD do. See?

This, then, is the difference between an unbalanced condition in a mental reaction and that of dementia—which destroys the reaction in the plasm of the nerve as fixed from the blood supply itself; though, unless there are some material changes, this may become the condition that will ensue.

The reactions, to be sure, began with the developments of the body in the eighth to twelfth year, and the shocks to the nervous system, with the inability of the blood supply to make the reactions that may be said to be the FULL ability for perfect coagulation—through SUGGESTIVE influences.

Hence a great deal of the condition existent in the present is psychopathic [psychological].

Hence the character of the hallucinations, and the inability of the body to bring the mental reactions for that the speech would imply—and that the activities of the body would do.

For, it is the body ATTEMPTING to assert its own soul's development under a suppression of the imaginative and desirous impulses, THROUGH these suppressions throughout the developing period of the body!

Reaching, then, that period when there is the change in the impulses that flow from the body through its creative forces, in the active principle of the body-mental and physical in itself, we have that of the nervous breakdown.

And, as we find, these conditions may be MATERIALLY aided. See?

We would change the surroundings, and the environs. And let them be as near to nature as is possible. And while the body should not be left alone at any period, until there is an equal balance in the mental and physical activities, it should be so—in its surroundings—that it is not only near to nature but has to DEPEND UPON itself for the NECESSITIES of its activity; in the preparation of foods, in the preparation of rests, and in the activities for the body.

THESE will make for responses that would bring about, as we find, a nearer normal balance.

And the environs should be where the body would not only be as near to nature as possible, but the sun, the sea, the sand, the pines or the woods, should all be a part of the surroundings—or nature itself, see? and wear as FEW clothes as possible; yet making for physical ACTIVITIES throughout the change.

In the surroundings there should be the suggestive forces that are constructive and spiritual, and creative in their activity for the body.

And we will find these will respond, in sixty to ninety days, to a near normal condition.

Ready for questions.

We would use also with these, when the suggestions are given in the association, a gentle massage over the whole of the cerebrospinal system; using also the WET Cell Battery (plain, see? but carrying the Gold). The positive anode should be of the copper, and attached to the 4th dorsal plexus. The negative anode carrying the Gold would be attached to the right and up an inch from the umbilicus plexus, or over the ASSIMILATING ganglia—from the lymph reaction in digestive system, so that the FOODS that are assimilated will create a constructive force in the blood supply, responding to the cells of the GLANDS in the body.

This appliance would be given each evening, in the beginning—for the first ten days—attached only ten minutes; the next ten days twenty minutes; the next ten days thirty minutes. Then we would rest a period of ten days, see? Then begin over again.

The massage would be not so much of the osteopathic or adjustment nature, but more of the NEUROPATHIC—or a gentle QUIETING of the nerves.

Let the diets be nerve and blood building; well balanced.

Q. What suggestion should be given the body?

A. The constructive forces. Of necessity, the suggestions will be according to who does the suggesting—and the response of the body to the suggestor, see?

Q. Would Virginia Beach be a good place for the body?

A. Excellent!

Q. Would her aunt, Mrs. [760], be a good person to be with her?

A. Excellent!

Q. If she is the one to give the suggestion, just what should she say?

A. Let's wait until she commences, first—and then we will check over these! We would check these conditions, through these same sources, every ten days.

We are through for the present.

The pattern of pathology here is so complex that I will wait until we have had the opportunity to examine a subsequent reading in this series before attempting to interpret how the physical, mental, and spiritual factors in this case interact to produce psychosis. Specifically, Cayce's explanation of the source and nature of her "hallucinations" is particularly important.

Directly, I do want to point out the full range of therapeutic interventions recommended in this reading. This reading recommended therapeutic milieu, companion therapy, electrotherapy with gold, a nerve- and blood-building diet, suggestive therapeutics, and spinal massage. The young woman was to be encouraged to depend upon herself. In other words, she was to be engaged to accept responsibility for taking care of herself to whatever degree her condition allowed. Cayce stated that in "sixty to ninety days" she could be brought to a "near normal condition." The implicit message was that as she improved, she needed encouragement to help herself.

The second reading in this series was given on September 28, 1933. Cayce noted a general improvement while recognizing that the "hallucinations" were still a problem. Suggestive therapeutics was recommended to address the hallucinations. Note the explicit descriptions of nerve pathology in this reading:

Yes, we have the body here, [386]; this we have had before.

As we find, the general conditions in the body are improved from that as we have had before. As the general health is improved, and the inclinations are for the physical functionings to become nearer to normal in their activities, it becomes more necessary to consider the activities of the glands that have caused—and do cause yet—disturbances in the coordination of the reactions in the physical forces of the body itself. There is produced the extravaganza in the activity of the mental forces, or the hallucinations appear, from the incoordinating of the cerebrospinal and the sympathetic reactions in the body. Or, there is what is ordinarily known as inflammation of the membrane through which nerve impulses pass, that tends to make for those irritations that produce a washing away—or a plethora—in the activity of same in its reaction.

Then, we will find that suggestions, with the applications of those vibrations that will REVIVE those flows of the ducts and glands that supply the proper conditions to these portions of the body, will make for a continued improvement in the mental reactions and the coordinations of the body also.

Hence, we would continue much in the same ways and manners that we have outlined.

When unusual conditions arise, as the activities where there are the supersensitive influences of outside forces upon the body, and these reactions take the form of hallucinations (from the normal reactions), then the quieting of the body through suggestion will be found much better than with the use of influences [drugs] that would deaden the nerve reactions and tend to increase (as time goes on) those influences from without.

Ready for questions.

Q. What suggestion should be given the body?

A. That the application of those influences in the system is creating a normal balance, and will surround the body, its functionings, its activities, with those forces that will prevent the recurrence of the conditions that have disturbed the body; and normalcy will ensue.

As we shall see in the third reading in this series, the content of the suggestion will become more explicit. In reading 386-2, the suggestive therapeutics focuses on creating more balance in the body so that "normalcy will ensue."

Note the reference to "supersensitive influences of outside forces upon the body" which Cayce cited as the source of the hallucinations. Ms. [386] described the hallucinations as intrusive voices which caused her to be afraid. In the question and answer period near the end of the second reading, the problem of the auditory hallucinations was posed to Cayce:

> Q. When she speaks of the hallucinations, what reply should be made to her that will do her the most good?
>
> A. WHATEVER may be used to quiet it at the time, until there are such associations or connections that these influences may be ridded from the system.
>
> Q. Does she really hear the things she speaks of, or what causes the hallucinations?
>
> A. We have just described how that the supersensitiveness of the nerve forces opens the body to such influences; or the body becomes what might be termed a human radio, but in giving expression to what is heard may often deflect what is actually said, felt or thought. For, thoughts are things! and they have their effect upon individuals, especially those that become supersensitive to outside influences! These are just as physical as sticking a pin in the hand!

The image of a "human radio" receiving thoughts and "outside influences" is quite fascinating. Here is a quote from a modern psychiatric diagnostic manual (DSM-III-R) describing the same process from a clinical viewpoint:

> Certain delusions are observed far more frequently in Schizophrenia than in other psychotic disorders. These include, for instance, the belief or experience that one's thoughts, as they occur, are broadcast from one's head to the external world so that others can hear them (thought broadcasting); that thoughts that are not one's own are inserted into one's mind (thought insertion); that thoughts have been removed from one's head (thought withdrawal); or that one's feeling, impulses, thoughts, or actions are not one's own, but are im-

posed by some external force (delusions of being controlled).

Clearly, the hallucinations experienced by this young woman and Cayce's explanation of these psychotic phenomena fall within the current clinical description of schizophrenic symptoms. However, Cayce seems to be saying that the process is more than merely nervous system dysfunction. He is suggesting that the nervous system dysfunction somehow allows the body to become supersensitive—psychic, if you will. In this case, the telepathic process became distorted as it operated through the abnormal nervous systems. This blending of pathology and the paranormal may be fairly common in schizophrenia. We will look more closely at the paranormal aspects of some psychotic symptoms in the next chapter.

For now, I want to take a moment to attempt to relate the complex causative factors in this case to the acute symptoms, particularly the hallucinations. Cayce stated that shocks to the nervous system during childhood (ages 8-12) altered the physiology of the body. This alteration effectively suppressed the mental development of the girl. Keep in mind that Cayce's view of the body/soul connection is quite literal. Mind manifests through the nervous systems while spirit is expressed through the glands. In this case, the "shocks to the nervous system" apparently disturbed these important connections.

As the young woman continued through the developmental process of puberty and early adulthood, the powerful changes in glandular functioning associated with this transition produced an unbalancing in the mental and imaginative forces of the body. Cayce described this condition as being supersensitive. Due to alterations in her mind and body, she became opened to "outside influences." Apparently, she became quite psychic. To be psychic when you are not ready for it is to be psychotic. In other words, she may have been having valid transpersonal experiences, yet they were overwhelming to her. She had no way to understand what was happening to her or constructively apply the information that intruded into her consciousness. Thus, the biochemical and psychosocial stressors during this person's childhood and adolescence made her vulnerable to acute psychosis.

The third reading for [386] was given on October 26, 1933. This reading continued to note general improvement and encouraged a continuation of the comprehensive treatment plan. I am including portions of this reading which allude to this progress in addition to providing an excellent example of an explicit hypnotic suggestion to be utilized during the treatments:

Yes, we have the body, [386]; this we have had before.

As we find, there are considerable changes in the general physical forces of the body since last we had same here, and these are for the betterment; if that which has been gained in the changes is taken advantage of when there is the resuming of the vibrations and the suggestions with the other administrations that have been given for the body in the matter of the diet, the activities, the exercises, and the like.

In taking advantage of the situation, then, we find that the conditions are as these:

There is still at times incoordination in the sympathetics through the activities to the cerebrospinal [nervous system] and to the sensory reactions (we are speaking from the physical angle entirely in the present, you see), yet there has been created—by the activities of the properties in the system [gold]—more of a stimul[us] to the coordinating reactions in the form of filaments of circulation through the activities of plasm in the nerve forces themselves, as well as a better application of the blood supply about those portions through which the nerve plasm operates.

Then, to keep these in balance and to guide these impulses, so that there may be a controlling of the impulse to the nerve system, we would—with the [spinal] manipulations and the applications made—give the suggestions for the body to respond in a normal way and manner in the impulses created by the vibrations that are set up from the elemental forces in the body. Such suggestions as this:

NOW THERE IS BEING CREATED IN THE IMPULSES FROM THE GANGLIA IN THE SYSTEM THE NORMAL REACTION TO THE SENSORY AND SYMPATHETIC SYSTEMS OF THE BODY. AND THIS IS BEING NORMALLY ACTED UPON BY THE VIBRATIONS, AND THE REACTIONS WILL BE A PERFECTLY NORMAL BALANCING IN THE MENTAL, PHYSICAL AND SPIRITUAL BEING OF THE BODY.

Ready for questions.

Q. When should the suggestions be given?

A. As the outline has been. When the manipulations and battery actions are being given. That means at the same time!

Q. Are the massage treatments being given in the proper manner?
A. If not, we would have told you about it!

In addition to the valuable information about suggestive thera-peutics, this reading contains an interesting physiological detail which may help us to understand the nature of the biological pa-thology in this case. Note Cayce's description of the "filaments of circulation through the activities of plasm in the nerve forces them-selves." To grasp the significance of these filaments and inflamed nerve membranes mentioned in reading 386-2, a very brief intro-duction to neuroanatomy is necessary.

The body's nervous systems have often been compared to elec-trical wiring. However, there is one major difference. The various "circuits" in these systems make connections at junctures between individual nerve cells. These junctures are called synapses. Synapses are spaces between the cells in which special chemicals produced in the nerve cells act as messengers between the cells. The chemi-cals are known as neurotransmitters. Many illnesses, including schizophrenia, are thought to result from abnormal neurotransmis-sion within the synapses of certain circuits within the brain. Spe-cifically, the neurotransmitter dopamine is widely recognized to be involved in the neuropathology of schizophrenia.

The powerful antipsychotic drugs currently used to treat schizo-phrenia are thought to affect the action of neurotransmitters such as dopamine in certain areas of the brain. The therapeutic effect of these drugs is thought to result from a "normalizing" of the bio-chemical processes within the synapses of these cells.

Incidentally, filaments resembling those described by Cayce have been described in modern histology textbooks:

> The synaptic cleft . . . is filled with tissue fluid containing materials . . . that can be seen in electron micrographs . . . fila-mentous structures are sometimes seen tranversing the cleft. This led Pfenniger to suggest that there are two layers of inter-cellular material in the synaptic cleft, each containing fine threads (perhaps macromolecules or molecular aggregates) that stick out from each synaptic membrane like bristles from a brush.

This quote comes from a textbook entitled *Histology* written by

Arthur Ham and David Cormack. It is strikingly similar to the numerous descriptions of nerve synapses provided by Cayce many years before the invention of the electron microscope.

In the case of [386], Cayce not only discussed pathology within the synapse between nerve cells, he also noted that " . . . there is what is ordinarily known as inflammation of the membrane through which nerve impulses pass . . . " So the readings clearly anticipated modern medical research into the neuropathology of schizophrenia and many other degenerative illnesses. The numerous descriptions of neurotransmission, nerve membrane pathology, and nerve plasms provide a remarkable insight into the anatomy and physiology of the nervous systems at the cellular level.

However, the readings differ from contemporary medical science on the means of healing nerve pathology. The electrotherapy advocated in the readings was directed at reestablishing normal neurotransmission by encouraging the body's natural processes for self-healing to be utilized.

Returning to the final reading given for Ms. [386], we can note that it was different in both tone and content from the earlier readings. Notably, there was little consideration given to the hallucinations, other that noting that there was "still at times the incoordinations in the sympathetics." The bulk of the reading addressed more mundane problems. She asked about her recurrent hay fever and colds, a kidney problem, irregular bowel movements, skin blemishes, weak arches in her feet, and peeling finger nails. She was still apparently feeling some depression during this period, but not to the extreme degree as before. Apparently, the acute psychotic episodes were not a major issue.

Her final reading closed with some general advice which we all could take to heart:

Q. Any other advice at this time?
A. Be joyous. Be happy at all times, and apply in the daily experience that which is not only a desire to be of help to someone else, but physically help others and it will help self the more—mentally and physically!

At this time, she had been receiving the treatments from her aunt in Virginia Beach for about three months. She returned home to Tennessee on November 13, 1933. Her parents attempted to provide the treatments as best they could for a few months. In contrast to the aunt's effective intervention, they had difficulty getting [386] to co-operate with the treatments. It is doubtful that the treatments were consistently provided. About a year later, her father reported that she seemed to be doing better with occasional brief relapses into psychotic episodes featuring the auditory hallucinations. Apparently, she was unable to return to a fully normal condition and no further correspondence is available in this case.

Some Key Points to Remember

Stress can take many forms. In this chapter, we have focused primarily on stress produced by excessive worrying and from stressful life events. In each case, stress was translated into physiological pathology resulting in psychosis.

The concept of diathesis/stress was reiterated in this chapter. In the first case study that we examined, we noted one form of diathesis that can make a person vulnerable to stress. In that particular case, a spinal injury was cited as a vulnerability factor which combined with excessive worrying led to a schizophrenic breakdown.

The final case study which we considered contained many fascinating facets including childhood trauma, pathological neurotransmission, and apparent psychic experiences. The paranormal features of this case serve as an excellent introduction to the second part of this book. We shall see that Edgar Cayce sometimes viewed so-called psychotic symptoms as valid experiences. A basic definition of psychosis is a loss of touch with reality. In such cases, Edgar Cayce would agree. However, he might also add that losing touch with this reality doesn't necessarily exclude the possibility of being in touch with other realities.

PART II

TRANSPERSONAL ASPECTS
OF SCHIZOPHRENIA

9

Kundalini Crisis
◆

THE TERMS DEMENTIA praecox and schizophrenia are of relatively recent origin when one takes the larger view. Throughout the ages peoples of all cultures have recognized insanity. It is the interpretation of the various forms of psychosis which sets the modern viewpoint apart as distinctive.

To appreciate this distinctiveness, we must take into consideration the worldview (and even the cosmic view or cosmology) of other cultures—both ancient and modern. At the crux of this distinction lie our beliefs about the origin of our species, the nature of reality, and the meaning of life.

Without going off onto an extensive philosophical tangent, I will simply point out that modern medical science (including psychiatry) is derived from and based upon a materialistic view of reality. That which is real is physical, or at least can be measured in a physical manner. From a materialistic viewpoint, reality is substantial.

This is no small point when we are determining someone's sanity. In fact, the clinical assessment procedures used to determine sanity are heavily weighted toward a materialistic interpretation of reality. As we noted in the last chapter, to be "out of touch" with material reality is by psychiatric definition, to be psychotic.

From a materialistic perspective, we are each basically a fortuitous conglomeration of biological systems created by the wondrous process of evolution. We are born, live for a while, and die—end of personal scenario. Therefore, the meaning of life is survival—survival of the individual as well as the species. Along the way, we have developed certain social behaviors which enhance our prospects of survival. This we label culture.

If a person is only a biological machine, one might expect that this machine could break down. Should the organic hardware of the nervous system develop flaws, one would expect aberrant thinking, exaggerated emotions, and inappropriate behaviors. The specific nature of the biological flaw determines the types of symptoms which will be exhibited. Hence we have the basis for a truly biological approach to mental illness—an outgrowth of the "medical model" of disease.

With mental illness reduced to the biochemistry of the brain, we need simply to ferret out the specific neurotransmitter system which is defective in each mental illness. Hence, in depression the flaw lies in nerves which utilize the neurotransmitters serotonin and noradrenaline. In Alzheimer's disease, the neurotransmitter acetylcholine is suspected to be at fault. In schizophrenia, problems with dopamine neurotransmission is considered to be the most likely source of the problem. Treatment revolves around correcting the brain's machinery with the appropriate drug at the optimum dosage.

The fact of the matter is, there is a great deal of truth (and effectiveness) in this approach. And as we shall see, this is exactly what one might expect based upon a holistic perspective of mental illness.

Yet there is a difference. From a holistic viewpoint, biology is only a substrate, as it were, of the human experience. It is only part of the equation of who we are, where we come from, and what the meaning of life is.

If we allow ourselves the opportunity to look around us (including looking backward in time), we see that the materialistic philosophy is not the only way of looking at life. In fact, it is not (and has never been) the philosophical position taken by the majority of human beings living at any given time. Of course, we can dismiss other viewpoints (even if they constitute the dominant overall human experience) by insisting that all other views are based on ignorance. However, before such an abrupt (and elitist) dismissal, let us lay out clearly some of these alternative beliefs about the ultimate nature of the human experience.

The Perennial Philosophy

The details of all the various alternative explanations of our origin and destiny are so extensive that it would take many volumes to lay out this record. Rest assured; I will not subject you to the endless meandering of philosophy and religion. What I will do is to attempt to lay before you some of the fundamental beliefs which are common to all of the major nonmaterialistic approaches. As I noted in the Introduction, the integration of these comparative studies has been called the perennial philosophy. In other words, the basic truths about the human condition are like perennial plants that are able to endure the trials imposed by various cultural settings. In a sense, the perennial philosophy represents the distillation of wisdom from the major philosophical and religious traditions of the world.

The most fundamental assertion of the perennial philosophy posits that there are nonmaterial aspects to reality. In fact, material reality has its source and sustenance in these nonmaterial aspects. As participants in this multidimensional creation, each human being is also more than a biological machine. These added dimensions have been called by many names: mind, soul, spirit, and so forth.

The concept of the continuity of consciousness is also central to the perennial philosophy. Apart from the birth, life, and death cycle of earthly existence, aspects of ourselves are immortal and carry over into other realms of consciousness. The variations on this theme are multitudinous. Reincarnation is a commonly held belief about the continuity of consciousness, although there are certainly many other ways of viewing it.

Within all versions of the perennial philosophy we find the idea of progress or evolution of consciousness. Images of rebirth and awakening are common. The earth experience is often viewed as a classroom in a school. The meaning of life is development. Life is meant to be a growth experience. We learn by a process of cause and effect by which we must be responsible for our actions. When the process of cause and effect stretches over many lifetimes, it may be referred to as karma.

Inherent within the perennial philosophy is the concept of the transpersonal. There is more to reality than our daily conscious experience of material life. There are realms of experience and states of consciousness that exceed the boundaries of our personalities. There is a creative force and higher power which is the source of "all that is." All of the above-mentioned aspects of the perennial philosophy are facets of the transpersonal—they take us beyond the sensory perception of ourselves as separate and distinct entities. Our personal selves are like tips of icebergs extending into unfathomable depths of consciousness.

We each make regular journeys into these depths during periods of sleep. We remember these excursions in the form of dreams. Significantly, researchers have noted the similarities between dreams and the psychotic symptoms of schizophrenia. Some theorists have even hypothesized that certain symptoms such as hallucinations are merely intrusions of the dream state into waking consciousness. In this view, certain forms of schizophrenia may be considered to be disruptions of the normal circadian rhythms which govern patterns of wakefulness and sleep. There is at least one example of such a pattern in the Cayce readings. In reading 600-1, a young man in the early stages of psychosis was told that a misalignment of his lower spine had affected his reproductive system producing "dreams or visions even in the waking state." Since schizophrenia is a diverse syndrome encompassing a variety of subgroups, perhaps dream intrusion into waking consciousness may account for some cases of psychosis.

Sleep and dreams are not the only access to the transpersonal realms of consciousness. Mystical states of consciousness may result from regular prayer, meditation, or religious devotion. They may even occur spontaneously or as the result of an unusual happening such as a "near-death experience." Whatever the trigger event, the transpersonal experience may resemble psychosis to an objective bystander. Remember that psychosis can be defined as a loss of touch with material reality. Many transpersonal experiences fall within the same definition.

The connection between insanity and transpersonal experiences has been amply noted. The well-known mythologist Joseph Campbell has observed that "the schizophrenic is drowning in the same waters in which the mystic swims with delight." Throughout the ages, persons experiencing religious ecstasy have been called "mad lovers of God." Among the Native Americans, individuals capable of entering psychotic states were revered as shamans. The list goes on and on. The point is that when we broaden our views as to what constitutes reality to include nonmaterial realms, diagnosing psychosis can become quite complicated.

What has the perennial philosophy to do with our exploration of the causes and treatment of schizophrenia? It is simply this. Schizophrenia, as it is currently defined, is a syndrome composed of various subgroups. According to numerous sources, including the Cayce readings, one or more of these subgroups may involve valid transpersonal experiences. It is even conceivable that many or most of the subgroups involve some aspects of transpersonal experience. In this chapter we will look at one such subgroup labeled kundalini crisis. In subsequent chapters, we shall note other aspects such as reincarnation, karma, and possession.

As a prime example of the perennial philosophy, the psychic readings of Edgar Cayce provide a fascinating opportunity to integrate the transpersonal dimensions of human experience (including psychosis) with the materialistic worldview. One of the major reasons that the readings offer this opportunity for integration is the explicit description of how the transpersonal aspects of the self connect with the physical body. For it is the interface between the transpersonal aspects of the self and the physical body that is most often disrupted in schizophrenia. Recognizing these connections is essential if we are to appreciate Edgar Cayce's view of the causes and treatment of schizophrenia.

The Body/Soul Connection

In describing the connection between the transpersonal aspects of the self and the physical body, the Cayce readings speak of a physical body, a mental body, and a spiritual body, each existing in its own realm yet overlapping (or at oneness with) the others. For the purposes of our present discussion, I will refer to these nonmaterial bodies (that is, the mental and spiritual) as the soul.

Naturally, the concept of soul has been widely recognized in the various interpretations of the perennial philosophy. The ancient Egyptians regarded the soul as a divine ray acting through a fluid-like compound in the body. Hindus have viewed the soul as a portion of the all-pervading Ether. The Chinese philosopher Lao-Tse (the founder of Toaism) believed that the soul has two aspects: a spiritual soul and a semi-material vital soul. Plato proposed a triune model in which the soul was composed of a divine, rational aspect of God; a mortal, animal part; and an intermediate, interactive aspect (will). Aristotle defined the soul as the living sentiency or consciousness of the body. Some early Roman philosophers adopted a triune model similar to Plato's in which the soul consists of spirit, intellect, and a vital aspect. The list of soul attributes is extensive and diverse.

Within this diversity, there are certain key similarities. The soul is typically seen as consisting of certain basic aspects (such as mind, will, and spirit). It is closely allied with or equivalent to a life force which animates the body. Most important for our present discussion, the soul is connected to the body at definite anatomical centers.

Again, these ancient sources recognized a range of possibilities. The Orientals spoke of whirling wheels of energy called chakras. A subtle energy nervous system called nadis is associated with these whirling centers. Through the chakras and nadis flows the life force or kundalini energy. Plato regarded the brain and spinal cord as the chief connections of the soul to the body. He thought that through these structures flowed the vital force of the soul (notice the similarity between the Hindu chakras, nadis, and kundalini and Plato's nervous system connections and the vital force). Incidentally, Cayce's model of the body/soul connection integrates these views by associating the chakras with the endocrine glands and the nadis with the nervous systems.

The ventricles of the brain were emphasized by numerous sources including Galen and St. Augustine. Perhaps the most famous view of the body/soul connection was held by a more recent historical figure, René Descartes. The famous French mathematician and philosopher proclaimed the pineal gland in the center of the head to be the seat of the soul. Not surprisingly, the pineal gland is located within the third ventricle of the brain.

Again, there is a pattern within the diversity. To simplify it to the most basic anatomical structures, one could say that most versions of the perennial philosophy emphasize the nervous system and endocrine glands as the connections between body and soul.

So when we define the soul as comprised of mental and spiritual bodies which connect with the physical body at definite anatomical centers, we are well within the parameters established by historical versions of the perennial philosophy. In fact, one of the primary strengths of the Cayce readings is their comprehensiveness in this regard. Whereas some versions of the perennial philosophy focus on particular nerve centers or glands as the linkage of body and soul, the readings are more inclusive. In other words, key glands and nerve plexus are cited as being connecting centers between body and soul. The functioning of this network of anatomical centers is orchestrated by the pineal gland. In a previous work (*The Treatment of Schizophrenia,* see the Appendix), I have labeled this network the "pineal system."

The relevance of this system to our discussion of schizophrenia lies in the location of the anatomical centers which comprise the body/soul connection. They are the same nerve plexus and glands which were repeatedly cited in the case studies in Part One of this book. The readings specifically noted the nerve plexus at the 4th lumbar, 9th dorsal and 3rd cervical as crucial contact points. The sympathetic nervous system contains enlarged ganglia at these plexus. Injury to one of these plexus (or to a nearby plexus which could cause a "reflex" reaction to one of these enlarged plexus) could then lead to mental symptoms such as hallucinations. Cayce actually spoke of the mental body as flowing through these areas.

The Leydig gland and gonads were also frequently mentioned in these case studies. Pressures directly upon these pelvic organs can also disrupt the connection with the mental and spiritual bodies.

Here is an excerpt from reading 294-141 which describes the pineal gland and its various connections through the body. Note the references to how disruption of these connections can result in "hallucinations." Also note in the final paragraph the connection in the pelvic organs, particularly the lyden gland:

First, this shows that there is innate in each physical individual that channel through which the psychic or the spiritual forces, that are manifest in material world, may function. They are known as glands, and affect the organs of the system . . .

Q. Please discuss in detail the functions of the pineal gland.

A. If this is discussed from the anatomical viewpoint, in the fetus as is begun in first of gestation, we find this may be termed as the builder. As is seen, the location of same is in the beginning in that of the center or the nucleus about which all of the matter takes its first form, and becomes the brain as is guiding or directing the building of the body as its development in the womb takes place. As it then reaches from the umbilical cord to the brain, there is builded that as is centered about same by the physical attributes of that progenerated from those bringing such an action into being. When there has reached that stage when there is the separation of same, the cord then being broken, this forms then its own basis in the lower portion of the brain, or cerebellum, and through the medulla oblongata to the central portion of the cerebrospinal cord itself is held intact, and with the removal of same, or pressure on same, the various forms of hallucinations are evident, whether in the developing stage or when it has reached the elderly or older years in an experience. Its functioning, then, is as that, of that, which makes for—or known as—the impulse or imaginative body. Hence one that may be called demented by others, who has hallucinations from a pressure in some portions, may be visioning that which to him is as real (though others may call him crazy) as to those who are supposed to have an even balance of their senses . . .

In this activity, then, as is seen, there is within the genital organs the activity through that as may be called the lyden gland, which has within itself that closed door, or open door, as makes for activity through that to the base of the brain, or the pineal gland—as is at the base of the brain itself—which opens up for its activities and associations to those other portions of the brain; that sends out its sensations either through the sensory organism or the sympathetic organism, or the purely physical organism . . .

So we have here a description of the pineal gland and its role maintaining the connection between body and soul. Note that the pineal's influence is extensive. It is regarded not only as a discrete glandular entity, but also as the focal point of a system including a portion of the spinal cord, sympathetic and sensory nervous systems, and the lyden (Leydig) gland in the reproductive tract.

Also note that pressure upon this system (such as spinal injury) can lead to hallucinations and other "demented" symptoms: "Hence one that may be called demented by others, who has hallucinations from a pressure in some portions, may be visioning that which to him is as real (though others may call him crazy) as to those who are supposed to have an even balance of their senses . . . " We have encountered several cases of this type of psychosis in previous chapters.

The Wondrous Pineal

I want to digress here for a moment and discuss some important research findings which have helped us appreciate the role of the pineal gland in regards to physical and mental health. It has only been within the last couple of decades that the pineal gland has been viewed as a major endocrine gland by modern medical science.

To the contrary, in other cultures the pineal gland has for many centuries been associated with paranormal phenomena and insanity. Eastern philosophies have tended to view the pineal as an important "chakra," which, if activated, opened the individual to psychic experiences and cosmic vision. Contemporaneous Western philosophies also attached mystical significance to the pineal. Theosophy is an excellent example of a recent philosophical movement placing great emphasis on the functioning of the pineal gland.

Western science has only recently become open to such an important role for the pineal gland. Medical researchers Miles and Philbrick have described the historical context for modern research into the role of the pineal gland in mental illness:

> The ancient Greeks considered the pineal as the seat of the soul, a concept extended by Descartes, who philosophically suggested that this unpaired cerebral structure would serve as an ideal point from which the soul could exercise its somatic functions. Descartes thus attributed to the pineal a prominent function in uniting the immortal soul with the body. Being influenced by this thesis, many 17th and 18th century physicians associated the pineal causally with "madness," a link that has been uncannily prophetic for the present day.

The reference to "unpaired cerebral structure" is an example of one of the many anatomical and physiological peculiarities of the pineal body. The brain exhibits a high degree of bilateral symmetry, a characteristic not shared by the pineal. It is not generally regarded as having left and right divisions. The pineal is a small, cone-shaped gland attached to the posterior ceiling of the third ventricle of the brain, suspended in the cerebrospinal fluid. Its location in the center of the brain, combined with its unique proclivity to calcify, make it a valuable landmark for neuroradiologists. Relative to total body weight, the pineal is small (50-150 mg in man), yet its relative blood flow is second only to the kidney. From an evolutionary standpoint, the pineal appears to correspond to the "third eye" in certain lizards. Recognition of the pineal as an active endocrine gland is a recent advancement since the highly sensitive bioassays required to detect pineal secretions are relatively new.

While study of the pineal is one of the "hot" areas in current medical research, such has not always been the case. In fact, only a few decades ago the pineal was viewed by the mainstream medical establishment as a vestigial organ. Along with the tonsils and appendix it was thought to be an evolutionary artifact. A curious yet unimportant lump of tissue in the center of the brain.

In fact, during Cayce's era this view was so prevalent that in the reading excerpt which we just examined (294-141) he called it a "mass without apparent functioning." Note the word apparent. For while its functioning may not have been apparent to the medical community, Cayce held a different view. He saw the pineal as a key regulator of mental processes. Repeatedly he referred to it as the "governor of mental impulses to the brain." He described its role in the growth and development of the human body throughout the life span—from conception to senility. He discussed how the pineal was involved in altered states of consciousness. The psychic process by which he was able to give the readings was contingent upon the activity of the pineal. The readings linked dysfunction of the pineal to numerous mental and physical conditions including schizophrenia, depression (both bipolar and unipolar), and epilepsy. Subsequent medical research has supported his viewpoints in all of these areas.

So, just as Cayce predicted several decades ago, when the pineal was widely viewed as a vestigial entity, current research has revealed it to be an important neuroendocrine gland involved in thermoregulation, immune response, and the mediation of various cycles (i.e., circadian rhythms involving the regulation of sleep, seasonal rhythms affecting patterns of reproduction and physiological adaptations to the environment, and cycles of growth and development during the life span such as sexual maturation). In consideration of the pineal's influence on the other endocrine glands, it has been proclaimed as a "regulator of regulators." Further, pineal functioning may play an important role in mental illnesses, such as schizophrenia, and mood disorders, such as the various forms of depression.

The phenomenal attention which has recently been focused on the pineal has led one leading researcher to observe: "After years of disregard the pineal has taken its place in mainstream biology and medicine. It is an organ of particular fascination in that it serves as an interface between the environment and the body." Ebadi is even more exuberant in his characterization of the explosion of recent interest in the lowly pineal:

> The pineal gland, viewed historically as a "sphincter to control the flow of thought," as the "seat of the soul," as a "third eye," and depicted more recently as a "neuroendocrine transducer organ," now promises to portray more complex physiological functions than originally believed and forecasts to reveal more extensive implications in pathological processes than once deemed possible . . . Future investigations should be directed toward comprehension of the functions of numerous neglected neurotransmitters and biological substances found in the pineal gland. The results of these investigations may bring forth multifunctional significance for [the] pineal gland not only in "temporal arrangement of various reproductive events" in mammals, in "rhythmical thermoregulatory process" in some ectotherms, and in "nightly pallor response" in amphibians, but also in major arenas of human suffering such as seizure disorders, sleep disorders, and behavioral abnormalities.

To emphasize the impact of pineal research in the arena of modern medical research, I will cite one more brief accolade on this once lowly gland:

> The human pineal is now under intensive investigation by various groups throughout the world. In the next few years we can confidently expect the physiological and pathological roles of this mysterious gland to be elucidated. The pineal which for Descartes was the seat of the mind and the immortal soul may yet turn out to be of interest for biological psychiatry. The pineal has been called a neuroendocrine transducer but it could one day be more accurately termed a psychosomatic transducer standing as a mediator on the boundary between soma and psyche. (Mullen et al., 1978, p. 370)

Before going on to the next section, I want to include one further excerpt from the readings to help clarify the role of the pineal in schizophrenia. The following selection, which comes from reading 281-24, illustrates how pressure within the pineal system can lead to dementia praecox:

As we have indicated, the body-physical is an atomic structure subject to the laws of its environment, its heredity, its soul development.

The activity of healing, then, is to create or make a balance in the necessary units of the influence or force that is set in motion as the body in the material form, through the motivative force of spiritual activity, sets in motion.

It is seen that each atom, each corpuscle, has within same the whole of the universe—with its own structure.

As for the physical body, this is made up of the elements of the various natures that keep same in its motion necessary for sustaining its equilibrium; as begun from its (the individual body's) first cause.

If in the atomic forces there becomes an overbalancing, an injury, a happening, an accident, there are certain atomic forces destroyed or others increased; that to the physical body become either such as to add to or take from the *élan vital* that makes for the motivative forces through that particular or individual activity . . .

There is the physical body, there is the mental body, there is the soul body. They are One, as the Trinity; yet these may find a manner of expression that is individual unto themselves. The body itself finds its own level in its own development. The mind, through anger, may make the body do that which is contrary to the better influences of same; it may make for a change in its environ, its surrounding, contrary to the laws of environment or hereditary forces that are a portion of the *élan vital* of each manifested body, with the spirit or the soul of the individual.

Then, through pressure upon some portion of the anatomical structure that would make for the disengaging of the natural flow of the mental body through the physical in its relationships to the soul influence, one may be dispossessed of the mind; thus ye say rightly he is "out of his mind."

Or, where there are certain types or characters of disease found in various portions of the body, there is the lack of the necessary *vital* for the resuscitating of the energies that carry

on through brain structural forces of a given body. Thus disintegration is produced, and ye call it dementia praecox—by the
very smoothing of the indentations necessary for the rotary
influence or vital force of the spirit within same to find expression. Thus derangements come.

Such, then, become possessed as of hearing voices, because
of their closeness to the borderland. Many of these are termed
deranged when they may have more of a closeness to the universal than one who may be standing nearby and commenting; yet they are awry when it comes to being normally
balanced or healthy for their activity in a material world.

Note here the variation in causes of psychosis. In certain cases
psychosis may result from "pressure upon some portion of the anatomical structure that would make for the disengaging of the natural flow of the mental body through the physical in its relationships
to the soul influence." In previous chapters, we have reviewed numerous case studies in which some form of spinal injury or other
physical condition produced such an effect upon the mental processes of the afflicted individuals.

In other cases, there is a "lack of the necessary *vital* for the resuscitating of the energies that carry on through brain structural forces
of a given body. Thus disintegration is produced, and ye call it dementia praecox . . . " In other words, through hereditary factors or
dysfunctions within the glands of the system, the body is unable to
provide the support which the brain needs to sustain a normal,
healthy state.

While we have seen several examples of each of these patterns in
previous case studies, we have not fully discussed the nature of the
"hallucinations" and "delusions" in these cases. According to the
readings, very often psychotic symptoms such as "hearing voices"
are actually valid transpersonal experiences. "Hence one that may
be called demented by others, who has hallucinations from a pressure in some portions, may be visioning that which to him is as real
(though others may call him crazy) as to those who are supposed to
have an even balance of their senses . . . " Whether Cayce meant that
hearing voices in this context represents a psychic experience or
discarnate possession is not clear. We will explore the possibility of
possession in schizophrenia in Chapter Twelve.

I want to be careful and again point out that schizophrenia as it is
currently defined is a heterogeneous syndrome. In other words,

simply because one is out of touch with what we could term "normal" physical reality does not automatically mean that he or she is in touch with the transpersonal. In many cases, the degree of brain deterioration prevents the individual from being in touch with any reality during a psychotic episode.

Recognizing cases involving valid transpersonal experiences is important because such instances may call for specific therapeutic interventions to address the pathology. In other words, if a person's spiritual centers are in a sense stuck open, treatments directed at moderating the flow of energy through the centers may be helpful. We will consider some of these interventions in the case studies which follow. First, we will consider the nature of the energy which flows through these centers.

The Concept of Kundalini

The *élan vital* or life force which was mentioned in reading 281-24 has been called by many names. The readings also use the term kundalini when speaking of this vital energy. For those readers interested in this aspect of the transpersonal, John White has put together an excellent anthology on kundalini (see Appendix). In *Kundalini, Evolution and Enlightenment* he states:

> Kundalini is the personal aspect of the universal life force named prana by the yogic tradition. This primal cosmic energy is akin, if not identical, to ch'i (Chinese), ki (Japanese), the Holy Spirit, and various other terms from cultures that identify a life force that is the source of all vital activity.

Over the centuries, numerous meditative disciplines have evolved to activate and harness this potent bioelectrical force. As a relatively recent representative of this transpersonal tradition, Edgar Cayce utilized the kundalini energy each time he gave a trance reading.

During these readings, Cayce often spoke of this life force or energy that permeates the body and is the basis for physical growth and development. This force is electrical in nature and may manifest at different levels of intensity. In its lower form (or as the readings often prefer, in the low vibration) this energy circulates through the body in a figure eight pattern. Perhaps this pattern is the same as that found in the acupuncture systems of various Oriental perspectives.

During meditation (or in certain cases of glandular dysfunction), this energy can become "supercharged" in intensity—that is, its vibratory rate is increased as it flows through the body. It is this raised vibration that Cayce typically associated with the term kundaline (note: kundalini/kundaline is spelled in numerous ways depending upon the source of the information).

When the life force is raised in vibration to a level designated as kundalini, the individual may experience various types of transpersonal phenomena such as clairvoyance, telepathy, out-of-body experiences, and so forth. In reading 4087-1, given for a six-year-old child, Cayce observed that in previous incarnations the "entity" or soul had acquired the ability to easily raise the kundalini force. Thus, in this incarnation he might readily develop the facility for clairvoyance and precognition:

> For as we find this entity has more than once been among those who were gifted with what is sometimes called second sight, or the superactivity of the third eye. Whenever there is the opening, then, of the lyden [Leydig] center and the kundaline forces from along the pineal, we find that there are visions of things to come, of things that are happening . . .

Note the reference here to the lyden and pineal centers in this excerpt. These two glands, which Cayce said were the seat of the soul in the physical body, are key components in the "pineal system." Readers may remember the numerous case studies in Part One which involved some form of activity or pathology with these important centers. When these glands are mentioned in a reading, some type of transpersonal experience or activity is frequently cited.

However, the kundalini energy is like a two-edged sword. Its awakening can lead to psychic perception and physical healing. Yet, if misdirected it can cause problems. Cayce provided this advice to a forty-four-year-old man in reading 5162-1:

> We would not make or take the exercises as to raise the kundaline forces in the body without leaving that kind of an experience that is of a nature to coordinate the activities of such exercises through the organs and centers of the body.
>
> Not that these are not good, but it is not very good to give a child a razor, not very good to use a razor to sharpen pencils and try to shave with same. So it is in the activities of those

who disregard the means to an end of bringing coordination to organs of the body.

Therefore, activating the kundalini force should be approached with a degree of caution. Normally, the process of raising this energy is a natural and healthy step in spiritual progression and can lead to enlightenment. However, in certain cases, the process can go dreadfully wrong. The various yogic systems for activating the kundalini recognize this potential danger and have built-in safeguards to preserve the physical and mental health of the initiate. In the West, we sometimes tend to minimize or bypass these safeguards in our eagerness for personal development. The results can be devastating. We shall now consider some examples of the pathology which can result from an improper raising of the kundalini energy—a condition which as been called "kundalini crisis."

Kundalini Crisis

Mrs. [3421] was thirty-nine years old when she received the first of two readings. In her letters, she stated that she had started experiencing her pathological symptoms twenty-three years previously (at about age sixteen). She described her problem as a form of possession in which a creature "tears my body to pieces unless I keep moving and exercising, the reaction of my nerves is maddening." Apparently, she was able to sleep only about one to three hours each night. She had been to many doctors who were unable to assist in relieving her symptoms.

Cayce's diagnosis was a complex one. There were problems within all three aspects of the self: physical, mental, and spiritual. Within the physical body, he noted misalignment of the lower portion of the spine. This combined with psychological (mental) problems and lack of spiritual direction led to a kundalini crisis:

> ... the pathological [subluxations in hip and coccyx] as well as psychological conditions must be considered with the mental conditions of the body. We find there has been the opening of the lyden (Leydig) gland, so that the kundaline forces move along the spine to the various centers that open with this attitude, or with these activities of the mental and spiritual forces of the body ... The psychological reaction is much like that as may be illustrated in one gaining much knowledge without

making practical application of it. It then forms its own concepts. Now we combine these two and we have that indicated here as possession of the body; gnawing, as it were, on all of the seven centers of the body, causing the inability for rest or even a concerted activity . . . Pathologically, we may find this center in the reproductive gland or activity of the body—the ovarian activity.

This woman had become heavily involved in the study of various metaphysical systems. In fact, in one of her later letters, she remarked:

This is to reply to your letter . . . asking our reason for dropping from your mailing list some time past . . . Our first interest has always been Theosophy, and somehow, we got involved in too many different interests. We didn't have time to read all the material coming in, nor did we feel that we could afford to subscribe for all of them, even though our good wishes are with all. So we dropped all other interests except Theosophy.

According to reading 3421-1, she had become unbalanced by the study of this material without bothering to apply it in her daily activities. Hence, "The psychological reaction is much like that as may be illustrated in one gaining much knowledge without making practical application of it. It then forms its own concepts."

When the readings spoke of the tremendous power of the mental body, they went beyond the cliche, "mind is the builder." Rather, Cayce repeatedly stated that "thoughts are real things." In other words, thinking involves powerful (albeit subtle) forms of energy. In this particular case, Edgar Cayce referred to these energy forms as a kind of "possession of the body; gnawing, as it were, on all of the seven centers of the body." In her second reading, he was careful to point out that the possession in this case was a matter of "positive possession" in which the "creature" that tormented her was "a creation of thy own mental and physical self." We will discuss the various aspects of possession in Chapter Twelve. For now, I want to stay focused on the source and nature of the pathology in this case.

Through concentrated study of the occult, Mrs. [3421] had activated the kundalini energy in her body. Due to physical pathology in her pelvic organs and the lack of practical application of the knowledge that she was accumulating, this intense bioelectrical energy became misdirected and out of control. Her subjective experience was that she was being attacked by an alien creature, rather than a creation of her own mental and physical self.

Her readings suggested that she correct the physical problems in her pelvic organs with hot packs and osteopathic adjustments. Electrotherapy was recommended with the stipulation that the period of its use be utilized for meditation.

She apparently attempted to apply the treatment recommendations with minimal results. Later she acknowledged that " . . . we didn't quite understand the explanations and directions, and so couldn't follow them more carefully or accurately. The osteopath couldn't understand, but did the very best he could."

So, this case might be described as a case of "kundaline crisis." The bizarre nature of this woman's "hallucinations" and "delusions," along with the onset of symptoms at age sixteen, would likely lead to a diagnosis of schizophrenia by current psychiatric criteria. Also note that the pattern of physical pathology parallels many other cases cited in previous chapters—misalignment of the lower spine and abnormalities in the pelvic organs.

Other Examples of "Kundalini Crisis"

Cayce often warned that raising the kundalini energy without proper care given to physical health, mental attitude, and spiritual ideals was dangerous and could lead to physical and mental symptoms. Here is a selection from reading 3428-1 emphasizing the importance of channeling and directing the kundalini energy into constructive daily activities:

> And here we find some of those conditions of which many bodies should be warned—the opening of centers in the body-spiritual without correctly directing same, which may oft lead to wrecking of the body-physical and sometimes mental . . .
>
> Q. Is the local center of the disease in the brain or some other part of the body?
>
> A. As indicated, it is in those centers—the seven centers of the body—where sympathetic and cerebrospinal coordinate the more; 1st, 2nd and 3rd cervical; 1st and 2nd dorsal; 5th and 6th dorsal; 9th dorsal; 11th and 12th dorsal; and through the lumbar and sacral areas. These are the sources. This is not infection—it is the lack of coordination between the impulses of

the mental self and the central nerve and blood supply.
Q. Does sexual expression or repression cause this condition, or have any effect on same?
A. This was a part of the beginnings of it; for when the lyden (Leydig) glands are opened, which are in the gonads—or the centers through which the expression of generation begins, they act directly upon the centers through the body. Unless these find expression they disintegrate, or through thy association cause dis-association in impulse and the central or body-nerves.

The pattern in this example is similar to the previous case of Mrs. [3421]. He had experimented with metaphysical pursuits and raised the kundalini energy but failed to direct it into constructive application. As a result, he was suffering from epilepsy.

The importance of maintaining the integrity of the nervous and glandular systems when raising the kundalini energy is consistent with Cayce's view of the body/soul connection. According to the readings, the life force utilizes these key biological systems as it flows through the body. Hence, an injury producing an obstruction or deflection of this flow could result in physical and mental symptoms. Spinal misalignment resulting in pressures upon the nerves was a common example of such pathology. The case of Mrs. [1749] represents a perfect example of physical pathology obstructing the flow of the kundalini resulting in mental illness:

> ... there has been the inclination for the body, through activities of the mental self in its anxiety, to raise or open the centers of the body through meditation and activity when the physical forces were not in the condition for such.
>
> This produced upon the nerve system, especially the sympathetic, what might be called a contaminated stream of negative reaction; causing or producing a nervous breakdown.

Looking Back to a Previous Case Study

Recall the case of Mr. [282] in Chapter Two. Remember that while this man was vulnerable due to an inherited predisposition to insanity, that his psychotic episode was triggered by his intense religious devotion. Prior to [282]'s breakdown, Edgar Cayce's oldest son, Hugh Lynn Cayce, wrote to his father describing [282]'s condition as a "strange twist which borders on religious fanaticism." The spiritual path for this young man contained some painful twists and turns. The raised energy level produced by the unleashing of the kundalini was too much for his system to manage. The treatments which were prescribed in his case were to "CLOSE as it were the centers through the system to the influences from without—which naturally produces a softening of the reaction between the impulses of the nerve forces themselves [dementia]." This man had "opened the centers" throughout his body leaving him vulnerable to "influences from without," an expression indicative of possession.

Examples of Kundalini Crisis in Contemporary Culture

The case of Gopi Krishna, a well-known researcher and writer, is an excellent example of "kundalini crisis." After years of daily meditation, he experienced a powerful awakening of the kundalini energy. For several years afterward, he struggled to gain control of this powerful force. Eventually, he was able to overcome the physical and mental tortures of his aberrant spiritual awakening. In retrospect, he described the potent psychological effects of kundalini crisis:

> The condition [kundalini awakening] denotes, from the evolutionary point of view, a physiologically mature system ripe for the experience, and a highly active Kundalini pressing both on the brain and the reproductive system. But the activity of Kundalini, when the system is not properly attuned, can be abortive and, in some cases, even morbid. In the former case [when the brain is not ready], the heightened consciousness is stained with complexes, anxiety, depression, fear, and other neurotic and paranoid conditions, which alternate with elevated blissful periods, visionary experiences, or creative moods. In the latter [when the reproductive system is dysfunctional], it manifests itself in the various hideous forms of psychosis, in the horrible depression, frenzied excitement, and wild delusions of the insane.

Thus, Krishna's emphasis on the enlightening properties of kundalini is balanced by his awareness of its destructive potential when awakened prematurely. As Krishna observes, in some cases the difference between the two is difficult to assess:

There is a close relationship between the psychotic and the mystic. In a mystic, there is a healthy flow of prana into the brain, and in the psychotic the flow is morbid. In fact, the mystic and the psychotic are two ends of the same process, and the ancient traditions class mad people as mad lovers of God, or something divine.

Dr. Sannella, a psychiatrist, also notes the dual manifestations of the kundalini experience:

I have also witnessed this regrettable tendency among those who have stumbled onto the kundalini experience. But this says nothing about the experience itself, which is not inherently regressive. On the contrary, I view the kundalini awakening as an experience that fundamentally serves self-transcendence and mind-transcendence.

In 1974 Sannella co-founded the Kundalini Clinic in San Francisco, a facility dedicated to helping persons undergoing sudden kundalini arousal.

The transformative potential of spiritual awakening with psychotic features (which we have designated as kundalini crisis) has been noted by Christina and Stanislav Grof and labeled "spiritual emergency." Christina's description of her spiritual emergency and Stanislav's clinical insight into the transformative potential of these experiences provide a valuable resource in this area. Their criteria for distinguishing between spiritual emergency and psychosis provide a helpful "yardstick" for clinical assessment.

Among favorable signs [indicating spiritual emergency] are a history of reasonable psychological, sexual, and social adjustment preceding the episode, the ability to consider the possibility that the process might originate in one's own psyche, enough trust to cooperate, and a willingness to honor the basic rules of treatment. Conversely, a lifelong history of serious psychological difficulties and of marginal sexual and social adjustment can generally be seen as suggesting caution. Similarly, a confused and poorly organized content of the experiences, presence of Bleuler's primary symptoms of schizophrenia, strong participation of manic elements, the systematic use of projection, and the presence of persecutory voices and delusions indicate that traditional approaches might be preferable. Strong destructive and self-destructive tendencies and violations of basic rules of treatment are further negative indicators.

Christina Grof founded the Spiritual Emergency Network (SEN) in 1980 to provide educational information and a referral service for people experiencing transformational crises. It is currently located at the Institute of Transpersonal Psychology (250 Oak Grove Ave., Menlo Park, CA 94025; 415/327-2776).

The story of Mariel Strauss provides a very personal glimpse into the phenomenon of kundalini crisis. She became involved in numerous "new age" activities including meditation. Evidently, her system could not handle the stress. Her familiarity with the Cayce material enabled her to relate her condition to the concepts presented in the readings. Her book, *Recovering from the New Age: Therapies for Kundalini Crisis,* documents the symptoms of kundalini arousal and suggests therapies to minimize its distress.

Thus, Strauss describes "kundalini crisis" from her personal experience, while providing a scholarly review of the kundalini literature. Her familiarity with the Cayce philosophy and frequent citations from the readings serve as valuable stepping-stones among the various sources and perspectives in this literature. Her recognition of the pervasiveness of kundalini manifestations, both clinically in psychosis and subclinically in "dis-ease," accurately portrays the readings' perspective of this phenomenon:

> We must remember that Cayce found degrees of kundalini imbalance in many individuals, not just in those with the syndrome of extreme symptoms we have delineated [i.e., kundalini crisis]. His cases ranged from those who were simply nervous and fatigued . . . to those who had been confined to hospitals or their homes for many years, sometimes since early childhood. Therefore, his remedies dealt less with large alterations in diet and more with the other aids . . . such as spinal adjustment and massage, mental regroupment, and treatments with the electrical appliances he designed.

Some Key Points to Remember

We have expanded our discussion of schizophrenia to include the concept of transpersonal experience as a source of certain psychotic symptoms. Some fundamentals of the perennial philosophy have been presented which lay a foundation for understanding key transpersonal aspects such as kundalini crisis, reincarnation, karma, and possession.

In this chapter we have focused on kundalini crisis, a form of premature spiritual awakening. To assist us in understanding the nature of this powerful transformative process, I have described the key elements of the body/soul connection. These connections (which have been called "centers" or chakras) form the physical gridwork, as it were, for the circulation of a bioelectrical life force. In its lower intensity, this life force is the source of growth and development. The intensity of the life force can be raised in many ways including certain forms of meditation, glandular dysfunctions, etc. When raised in intensity, it is called kundalini.

We have reviewed several examples where kundalini awakening has resulted in the symptoms of mental illness. Several factors were noted as contributing to kundalini crisis. Extreme religious or metaphysical involvement combined with a weakened physical condition was a common pattern. Lack of spiritual direction or constructive daily application of occult knowledge was also frequently cited as a cause of kundalini crisis.

We have seen that the concept of kundalini is widely accepted in Eastern metaphysical traditions. It is gaining a broader acceptance in Western culture with the increase in meditative practices and interest in metaphysical studies. Consequently, we have noted that the phenomenon of kundalini crisis has been addressed in the contemporary psychiatric literature.

If readers care to review the case studies in Part One, they will probably recognize transpersonal features in some of the cases. A close examination of these cases will usually correlate closely with the concepts and terminology presented in this chapter. For example, the involvement of the lyden (or Leydig) and pineal glands is significant. Cayce identified these organs as the "seat of the soul" in the human body. The references to "centers" in the body is also significant because mind and spirit manifest through definite anatomical structures and physiological processes. We may therefore appreciate the importance placed upon maintaining the integrity and coordination of these centers represented by the nerve ganglia along the spine and the endocrine glands. The readings' frequent linkage of spinal injuries (particularly of the lower spine) and pelvic disorders with schizophrenia makes more sense when we expand our view of the human experience to include the transpersonal aspects associated with these centers.

Thus, there are two important points to consider here. One is that persons undergoing a kundalini crisis might be diagnosed as suffering from schizophrenia and treated accordingly. The biological and psychosocial repercussions from this misunderstanding could be very unfortunate. Rather than leading to personal development, the crisis could cause the person to become ensnared in a mental health system that has no sympathy for transpersonal experiences. Stigma and medication side effects are two of the worst facets of this type of misunderstanding.

A second important point is that persons who are undeniably suffering from schizophrenia may also have some transpersonal features blended into their psychosis. Keep in mind that the kundalini energy may be activated in numerous ways besides classical yogic disciplines. Some of the forms of biological deterioration that are associated with schizophrenia may also make the person vulnerable to kundalini arousal. So even though a person may be suffering from a definite schizophrenic disorder (which may involve brain degeneration), some of the symptoms may have a valid transpersonal dimension. As Cayce and other traditional sources have noted, such individuals may be nearer to God than the health care professionals who are providing supportive services. I will address some of the clinical implications of dealing with transpersonal symptoms in the last chapter.

Anxiety is another frequent symptom of kundalini crisis. I have written a book documenting case studies of anxiety recorded in the Cayce material. It is entitled *Living Nightmares*. It contains a chapter which examines the various aspects of anxiety which can accompany kundalini awakening. Readers interested in this topic may wish to avail themselves of this resource.

This chapter has been rather lengthy with an emphasis on explaining the nature of the transpersonal. This was necessary so that readers could have an appreciation of the concept of kundalini crisis as well as provide a foundation for the material which follows. In the next chapter we will further consider the transpersonal dimensions of mental illness. We will look at the idea of reincarnational "bleed-throughs" as a possible source of some of the hallucinations and delusions associated with schizophrenia.

10

Reincarnation

◆

As we noted in the previous chapter, the continuity of consciousness is a fundamental premise of the perennial philosophy. Reincarnation is one of the most common and comprehensive explanations of this continuity. Granted, it is not the only explanation. It is beyond the scope of this book to do a comparative study of the various ways of looking at the eternalness of our being. I merely want to present reincarnation in a way that will help us to understand some cases of schizophrenia in which the readings mentioned past-life experiences as relevant to the individual's psychosis.

There are two aspects of reincarnation which I want to cover. In this chapter I will present information about how the opening of the spiritual centers and raising of the kundalini can open up a person to past-life memories. The recall of such memories would probably be interpreted by most mental health professionals as hallucinations and/or delusions. I did not include these cases in the last chapter because it seems evident that the degree of pathology clearly exceeds the domain of kundalini crisis. In other words, I think it unlikely that anyone would interpret such symptoms as side effects of spiritual transformation.

The second aspect of reincarnation which is relevant to our understanding of schizophrenia is karma. Karma addresses the question of causation. Certainly, the cases in this chapter may involve significant karma. However, presently I want to focus on the clinical features of past-life recall and reserve the issue of cause and effect until the next chapter.

In this chapter, we will focus primarily on two cases in which past-life memories seemed to "bleed through" into present states of consciousness. The individuals experiencing these past-life memories could not differentiate between the past and present. Clearly, such a person would be diagnosed as psychotic—or as being out of touch with reality.

"Other Appearances in the Earth"

The parents of Ms. [5274] had many questions concerning their daughter's problems. At the top of the list were inquiries which one might expect in a case of major mental illness. As this woman was confined in a mental institution, it was natural to ask, "Why does she have an uncontrollable temper and refuse to cooperate with doctors and nurses in hospital?" If she persisted in her oppositional behaviors, there was little hope for recovery. Which brings us to the second question, "Is there any chance of rehabilitation?" As we shall see, Edgar Cayce addressed both these questions in reading 5274-1.

However, the fascinating questions in this case related to her "hallucinations" and insistence on wearing a pad over her right eye. In answering this question, Edgar Cayce cited a transpersonal aspect to this woman's psychotic delusions.

Reading 5274-1 was given on May 17, 1944. As was typical of readings given in the months near the end of Edgar Cayce's life, the reading was extremely concise:

> Yes, we have the body and those conditions which are disturbing the better physical and mental conditions of this body.
> As we find, there are disturbances, but whether these will respond to the applications that may be suggested will depend a great deal upon the faith and hope and persistency of the parents, for this has gone on for so long.
> There are pressures in the coccyx end of the spine from an

injury received thirty-seven years ago. This has become static.

We would do this: Have those corrections and coordinate the segments in lumbar, throughout the dorsal area, especially the 9th and 10th dorsal, 6th, 7th, 5th, 4th, 3rd dorsals and through the cervical.

Then add the low electrical forces of the Wet Cell Appliance used as a Radio-Active [Appliance].

Thus we may get response if there are prayers and activities of those about the body in the way of patience, persistency and consistency.

Ready for questions.

Q. Should she be left in an institution or return to her home . . . ?

A. It cannot be done in an institution.

Q. What causes the hallucinations and the persisting in wearing a cardboard or metal pad above her right eye?

A. These are the reactions from former appearances of the same entity in the earth.

Q. Why does she imagine she is being abandoned and tortured by people who dislike her?

A. This, again, is the impression from other appearances in the earth. Do these that have been indicated. It will require long periods and patience. Do have the corrections made osteopathically. Have them made in this manner: Align the whole cerebrospinal system, with special attention to the coccyx area, and have at least ten or twelve, then leave off for a month or six weeks, but keep up daily the use of the low Wet Cell Appliance used as a Radio-Active [Appliance], to be used thirty minutes each day. Use this when the body is ready to retire. Let the parents make the suggestions as the body sleeps, not as the body arouses or awakens, but with the Appliance on as the body sleeps. Normalcy and love and care of parents is due every child.

We are through with this reading.

This woman was thirty-nine years old when the reading was given. If Cayce was correct in describing the source of the physical pathology as an accident thirty-seven years previously, the injury to the coccyx (tailbone) would have occurred in her second year.

Naturally, the therapeutic recommendations focused heavily on relieving the pressures along the spine. As was so often recom-

mended, he also advised that electrotherapy and suggestive therapeutics be used. This is an important point. The therapies recommended in cases involving transpersonal features are essentially the
same as for other cases of schizophrenia. I will follow up on this
point in the final chapter.

Of course, it was essential that she be removed from the hospital
because such treatments would not be available in that setting. Perhaps this suggestion was also directed towards the parents. Cayce
was typically reticent to disclose information about childhood
abuse or neglect in such cases. So one cannot be sure whether he is
simply emphasizing the need for a therapeutic milieu or discreetly
acknowledging past shortcomings on the part of the parents. As he
noted, "Normalcy and love and care of parents is due every child."

The reincarnational aspects of this case leave much to the imagination. The theme of abandonment and torture apparently carried
over into her present consciousness. In her mind, these past episodes of pain were a constant reality. She saw the people around her
as her torturers. Perhaps they were, in a past life. Or, considering the
high level of patient abuse and neglect which was prevalent in many
mental institutions during the early decades of this century, maybe
these torturous conditions only triggered past-life memories or associations.

At any rate, no further communications were received in this
case. It is unlikely the recommendations were applied.

"Experiences Through Which the Entity in Transition Has Passed"

Our second case study in past-life recall involves a twenty-eight-
year-old woman who experienced recurrent breakdowns and was
hospitalized at the time of her reading. Her brother wrote to Edgar
Cayce describing her condition and requesting a reading.

> She is a psychopathic case at Eloise Hospital at present and
> has been there since 11/2/39. We don't know what caused the
> collapse, or whatever it may be, because she seems to remem-
> ber everything said to her from one visit to the next and yet she
> cannot carry on a normal life . . .
> On 10/31/39 she became violent while at work—was taken
> to the City Hospital until arrangements were made to transfer
> her to the Eloise Hospital on 11/2/39. Since then she has been

given all the known treatments for a physiological case. She improved after a year or so of the treatment and was released, but in less than a month she broke down again while on the streetcar. Fortunately she did not become violent against the passengers, but started to yell and kick at the exit doors. She was taken to the City Hospital and then transferred to Eloise again. Since then she has been getting worse all the time. At present she won't talk to anyone and becomes violent if anyone speaks to her. As far as the doctors know they can't do anything for her. What brought on the mental breakdown? Is there any possible cure for it? What can be done to help her?

As with the previous case study, a single reading was given near the end of Edgar Cayce's life (March 28, 1944). Readers should readily recognize the pattern of pathology in this case as it parallels that of many cases in earlier chapters—pressures along the lower spine, adhesions in the pelvic organs, and involvement of the lyden and pineal glands:

Yes, we have the body and those conditions that are a part of the experience of the entity [4002].

As we find, there are very definite causes that produce the abnormal reactions between the mental and the imaginative or the sympathetic and imaginative reactions to the brain.

These have been existent some time.

We find that there are adhesions in the organs of the pelvis causing definite reactions to the pineal gland. These as they react to and through the reflexes of brain cause those periods when there are the exaggerated repressions, and there enters all of those experiences through which the entity in transition has passed.

Thus the reactions sound abnormal, they become ridiculous to many.

The attempt of the physical body to react to same produces violence to others.

As we find, if there would be the application of the short-wave electrical shocks for the body, along with the osteopathic adjustments that might be made in Macon, Missouri [Still-Hildreth Osteopathic Sanatorium], there might be brought back near to normal conditions for this body—with the rest, with gentleness, kindness, and the assurance physically and spiritually.

Ready for questions.
Q. What specific areas need correcting?
A. Through the lumbar, sacral and lower dorsals.
Q. What brought on the mental breakdown?
A. As just indicated the adhesions in the pelvic organs, as directly connected or associated with the lyden (Leydig) and the pineal glands. Do these things and we will bring better conditions for this body.
We are through with this reading.

"Transition" is a key word in this reading. Cayce often spoke of birth and death as simply transitions from one plane of reality or consciousness to another. He described death as passing through a doorway, as going from one room to another. Death in one plane means birth into some other realm. This transition process is an important part of the continuity of consciousness which is central to the transpersonal perspective.

Certainly, it is understandable that if this young woman was vividly recalling past-life memories and experiencing them as real in the present, her actions would be perceived as "abnormal" and "ridiculous" by family and caregivers. As with the previous case study, this woman was apparently capable of becoming quite agitated, even violent. She remained in the hospital and Cayce's recommendations were ignored.

The physical pathology in this case is significant. It parallels the first case study in this chapter and the discussion of kundalini crisis in Chapter Nine. Recall that we defined kundalini crisis as a syndrome produced by inappropriate raising of the vibratory life force. Kundalini crisis was usually associated with misdirected attempts at spiritual awakening through various spiritual disciplines and activities. According to Cayce, it could also be activated through certain kinds of injury or disease. As with cases of spiritual awakening, the pineal system would become activated and the kundalini energy would surge through the centers of the body. If this energy was not directed toward constructive application or if the body were weakened and not able to handle the stress of this potent force, mental and physical symptoms could result.

Past-life recall was one of the extraordinary transpersonal experiences which this kundalini awakening could arouse. Reading 5399-2 was given for a twenty-eight-year-old woman who was having just such a paranormal experience:

Q. Have I ever caught glimpses of past lives, or are these things more dreams and fancy?

A. The entity has caught glimpses of past lives when it has gone out of itself or has allowed the energies of the kundaline force to pass along the centers of the body. Beware unless you are well balanced in your purposes . . .

In our modern culture, many people actively seek such experiences. There is a strong interest in exploring past lives for growth and development (i.e., the "new age" movement) as well as a therapeutic technique (past-life hypnotherapy). If such persons are "well balanced" in their purposes and ready for the experience, past-life recall can have tremendous transformative effects.

However, place yourself in the position of the two individuals that we have discussed in this chapter. The two women whose cases we have examined were not consciously seeking such experiences. To the contrary, the intrusion of past-life memories must have been extremely disorienting. To have such powerful, emotion-laden memories flooding over their consciousness would have been a real experience to them while appearing psychotic to others. Again, we are left to ponder the question of what is reality.

Some Key Points to Remember

In this chapter we have reviewed two cases involving psychotic features which, according to the readings, were associated with past-life recall. The pattern of pathology in these cases closely resembles cases of kundalini crisis discussed in Chapter Nine. Presumably, pressures to the lower spine affecting the pelvic organs (specifically the lyden gland) caused the kundalini energy to become activated. Transpersonal experiences of a psychic nature resulted.

In contrast to the cases of kundalini crisis discussed in the previous chapter, the women reliving these past lives were not engaged in attempts to awaken the kundalini. Rather, they were the unfortunate victims of physical pathologies which altered their body's energy systems and launched them into psychosis. However, the treatment regimens in both cases were essentially the same as for most of the cases which we have reviewed in previous chapters.

11

Karma

———◆———

As WE HAVE seen, the Cayce readings present a panoramic view of the human condition which, in certain respects, parallels the primary Eastern religions and philosophies (particularly Hinduism, Buddhism, and Taoism). From this perspective each individual is regarded as an immortal being evolving toward unity with the divine source of being. While the path to this reunification is uncertain, the eventual destiny is assured.

The continuity of consciousness is a fundamental premise of this perspective. As we have noted, this view typically includes reincarnation or some other developmental process which acknowledges the immortality of each individual. At the center of the developmental process is choice or, if you prefer, free will. However, present choices (or opportunities) are not totally free. They are limited or defined in terms of previous choices. We are today the sum total of all our previous choices and actions. This is cause and effect. When the action and reaction process extends over lifetimes, it is called karma. The readings are in total agreement with the biblical scriptures and Eastern religions on this point—we reap what we sow. Therefore, karma is not something to be viewed as punishment for past errors. Rather it is presented in the readings as an opportunity to learn from our past successes and mistakes.

Naturally, one wonders how karma actually works in specific cases of severe illness such as schizophrenia. In other words, how do the patterns of cause and effect bridge the gap from lifetime to lifetime?

The Role of Heredity and Environment in Karmic Patterns

The readings present several possible answers to this difficult question. At the head of the list is heredity. After all, biological heredity provides a relatively stable and predictable means of having the necessary life experiences to encounter one's karma. The readings state that individuals are drawn to incarnate in physical bodies which provide a high probability that they will "meet themselves"— an expression often used in cases of karma. Therefore, heredity is an effective way of providing the high probabilities necessary for karmic interactions.

However, this is not to say that every hereditary pattern is necessarily karmic. The human condition is much more dynamic in its unfoldment. It is also much more creative. In other words, there are many ways that karmic patterns can manifest. It is generally true that pathological karmic patterns tend to manifest rather early— during gestation, birth, or early childhood.

Environmental influences also figure heavily in cases involving karma. Again, these factors provide a relatively stable framework in which certain key probabilities can unfold. The traits of the parents are well established when the child enters the scene. For better or worse, the drama is played out.

In clinical terms, karmically associated patterns are usually particularly difficult conditions to heal. Karma often involves deep biological pathology (e.g. heredity) or psychosocial abnormalities (e.g., neglect or abuse). In such instances Cayce often noted that the spiritual aspects of treatment would play a crucial role in achieving a constructive result. In such cases, Cayce would often comment, "the entity is meeting self" and caution the person to use the experience as a stepping-stone rather that a stumbling block.

From a theoretical perspective, karma provides a link between key concepts such as choice, responsibility, and the continuity of consciousness. Karma is the impetus for growth and development on all levels. As a fundamental law of the universe, karma insures that we will all find our way back to our Creator, one way or another.

Not surprisingly, karmic conditions often involved the glandular system, which Cayce viewed as the spiritual connection within the physical body. Several of the individuals diagnosed by Cayce as suffering from karmically linked dementia praecox apparently had glandular problems. In these cases, karma was often a family affair where the care of the afflicted person was a karmic responsibility of the parents or guardians. Spiritual suggestions were prominent in these readings.

"Deeper or Reincarnated Influences"

The first case study which we will examine contains both strong environmental and hereditary factors which predisposed a young man to nervous breakdowns and many years in mental institutions. Mr. [300] was thirty-five years old when he received a reading from Edgar Cayce. He had spent over ten years in a state mental institution. A doctor familiar with Edgar Cayce's work took an interest in the case. Prior to the reading, the doctor wrote to Cayce describing the man's situation. In part, he stated:

> . . . [300]'s home environment was very uninviting. His mother died early and his father drank himself into an early grave. He lived with his grandmother, whose mental faculty had deteriorated. He received a rather concentrated religious education in the Catholic church . . . I met him, for the first time, about eight or nine years ago. He was then a patient in one of our state institutions for the mentally sick. He was very blue, taciturn, and given to spending most of his waking moments in offering prayers in line with what he had been taught from early youth up. This last description fits his condition very much at the present day.

The doctor went on to describe how Mr. [300] was poorly motivated and was unable to care for himself—even prior to his hospitalization. The man was also prone to delusions of grandiosity employing the religious themes of his childhood education.

Edgar Cayce provided one reading for this man on March 16,

1933. In the first few paragraphs of this reading, Cayce noted that a better understanding of the condition could be gained through considering the transpersonal aspects (the "deeper or reincarnated influences") of the case which manifested as hereditary and environmental factors in the present earthly life:

> Now, as we find, in analyzing or describing those conditions that disturb this body and the mental body, much that has had and does have to do with the impetus or surroundings that brought the body into its mental and physical development would have to be analyzed—for these conditions to be materially aided.
>
> However, from a metaphysical as well as some particular conditions the case might be better understood; and in particular offer an opportunity or channel for the study of deeper or reincarnated influences, that go for the hereditary and environmental influence.
>
> In the present, however, we deal with the purely mental and physical manifestations that we find in this body at present, and what—as we find—may be done at present about the condition . . .
>
> Then, having been an entity, a body (in the present) with those surroundings or environs that brought about the warping of the instinct and intelligency of the active forces that coordinate with the imaginative and the material influences, we find an incoordination between the mental images as builded by the body and those that are able to be raised from the invisible to the visible as manifesting in a material plane . . . the abilities to coordinate the mental from the activities visible to material conditions or aids are almost nil . . . Or, there is little of the first impulse that are towards normalcy; that is, of self-preservation. To go into the pathological conditions for the moment, then, that they may be better understood, these are lacking in those centers along the sympathetic and cerebrospinal [nervous systems] where there are the coordinations between the [nerve] impulse and the stamen that cares for the abilities to carry on in a given line or direction.

So while the reading did not go into the details of the "deeper or reincarnated influences" that were the source of the hereditary and environmental factors, we are informed that there is a larger context to this man's mental illness. In some of the case studies which follow, Edgar Cayce actually provided "life readings" for individuals later diagnosed as suffering from schizophrenia. In those cases, details were disclosed about particular past lives and the source of the karma. For Mr. [300], this information was not forthcoming.

The therapeutic recommendations in this case focused on suggestive therapeutics. Specifically, the doctor was to give positive suggestions at definite periods once or twice a week. The good character of the caregiver was crucial in this case:

> Such suggestion may be best directed by one knowing the environs, the surroundings, the conditions that are to be met day by day. But, as given through these channels, only one that has the desire within self for the producing of a manifestation of God's love, and in a loving manner present such, as to bring the correct or proper conditions. See?

The expression "one knowing . . . conditions that are to be met day by day" is important in the application of suggestive therapeutics. The person giving the suggestions must be aware of the innerpersonal and interpersonal problems which must be addressed by suggestion. Only then can the suggestions be given in a way that addresses the particular issues which are relevant to the afflicted individual.

A very unusual thing happened at the conclusion of reading 300-1. About five minutes after the reading, when Gertrude Cayce gave the suggestion for Edgar to wake up, he suddenly resumed the reading with the following advice for the doctor:

> In making or beginning the application to [300], it would be well that suggestive magnetic treatments or therapeutics be begun. Letting the body lie prone, easy, quiet, place the left hand on the spine at the sympathetic or secondary cardiac plexus (4th, 5th dorsal), the palm of the hand covering this area. Resting a minute, then gently place the right hand (or palm) over the third eye—or that area just above the real face, or between the eyes and above the bridge of the nose. Then have the body gently relax, with the suggestions gradually given in monotone that makes the power of perception become more active through all [nerve] plexuses of the system. For, these will aid in not only quieting the body, but in enabling

the operator to guide, direct, in that necessary for the mental betterment.

Upon providing this additional information, Edgar Cayce did not wait for the suggestion to wake up. In fact, he jumped up from the couch wide awake. When asked what had happened, he said something seemed to be after him. He felt badly for quite a while after this reading.

The recommendation for "suggestive magnetic treatments" combined two therapeutic modalities. We have mentioned suggestive therapeutics in many of the case studies of schizophrenia. Magnetic treatment was a form of "laying on of hands" and was recommended for numerous disorders. The doctor was to combine the two therapies.

In subsequent correspondence the doctor noted significant improvement in response to the treatments. In a letter dated January 16, 1934, he stated: "[300] is in my opinion very much better. He has taken to make himself very helpful in the institution that is taking care of his physical needs." Two months later, the doctor wrote again describing [300]'s progress:

It might please you to learn some news of [300]. All in all, it is evident that he is on the upward grade. He has decided to make himself useful to the fellows in his ward and renders service to the best of his ability. In my opinion this is quite a splendid change. He talks with considerable more compassion and while his peculiar complexes are still noticeable at times in that he segregates himself for prayer on his knees, according to his early training in the Catholic church, he does not make himself obnoxious or difficult to get on with. He delights to keep himself clean, his clothing looking well, and to improve his vocabulary.

Four months later, [300]'s sister wrote to Edgar Cayce stating: "Have been in . . . and saw my brother [300] who, by the way, is greatly improved. I'm so thankful." There is no further correspondence to note until February 2, 1960, when a routine mailing brought a return card stating that [300] was living in a residential section of Cleveland, apparently doing well.

"A Beethoven or a Whittier or a Jesse James"

Our next case study is derived from a life reading given for a child. Life readings were one of several basic formats which Cayce utilized to provide information about the various aspects of the human condition. Most of the readings which we have reviewed to this point have been physical readings (which dealt with the biological dimension of illness). Life readings typically shifted the focus from the biological to the psychological and spiritual dimensions—to the journey of each soul through eternity. As part of this expansive discourse, Cayce would usually describe several past lives which were affecting the present life. He would also provide information about the soul's adventures in other realms of consciousness apart from earthly existence.

As a prelude to the reading, a conductor (usually his wife, Gertrude Cayce) would provide the hypnotic suggestion which would direct his search for the particular type of information which was being requested. On January 25, 1944, he gave a life reading, 3633-1, for an eleven-year-old boy. The standard suggestion was given by Mrs. Cayce and I will include it here to point out an important reincarnational concept:

> Mrs. Cayce: You will give the relations of this entity and the universe, and the universal forces; giving the conditions which are as personalities, latent and exhibited in the present life; also the former appearances in the earth plane, giving time, place and the name, and that in each life which built or retarded the development for the entity; giving the abilities of the present entity, that to which it may attain, and how. You will answer the questions, as I ask them.

Note the expression "personalities, latent and exhibited in the present life." In explaining the role of past lives, Edgar Cayce stated that past-life experiences tended to be carried over into a present life as personality traits. Some of these traits were "latent." In other words, they were just under the surface, ready to be expressed when the appropriate associations triggered them into action. Other traits were "exhibited." When exhibited, the past-life influence was active and conspicuous as a prominent personality style.

Another way of thinking about this is that we are each multiple personalities. Most of us make subtle shifts from one personality style to another. Sometimes the shifts are not so subtle. This view of personality as a cooperative venture of various aspects of the self is receiving considerable attention in the field of psychology.

In cases of pathological multiple personality, the various aspects of the self become isolated from each other and assume separate distinctive identities. Childhood abuse has been consistently linked to this aberrant form of multiple selves.

In life reading 3633-1, Cayce noted the divergent tendencies latent within the personality structure of this child:

> In giving the interpretations of the records here of this entity, it would be very easy to interpret same either in a very optimistic or a very pessimistic vein. For there are great possibilities and great obstacles. But know, in either case, the real lesson is within self. For here is the opportunity for an entity (while comparisons are odious, these would be good comparisons) to be either a Beethoven or a Whittier or a Jesse James or some such entity! For the entity is inclined to think more highly of himself than he ought to think, as would be indicated. That's what these three individuals did, in themselves. As to the application made of it, depends upon the individual self.

He went on to note that the parents would have to be "firm and positive with the entity, inducing the entity through reason to analyze self to form the proper concepts of ideals and purposes." If this could be accomplished, the parents would give to the world a "real individual with genius." Without this direction, "we will give to the world one of genius in making trouble for somebody."

The reading went on to detail several past lives where the entity had used his exceptional abilities for good and evil. On the negative side, there was a pattern of selfishness and indulgence.

The karmic aspect in this case is evident in the expression, "But know, in either case, the real lesson is within self." This phrase acknowledges that life on earth is a learning experience—the earth itself being like a classroom in a school. The lessons have mostly to do with making choices and acting on those choices. Poor choices (failed lessons) must be done again and again until the lesson is learned. This is why the readings so often used the expression "the entity is meeting self" in cases involving a heavy karmic pattern.

Upon receiving the reading, the parents of [3633] acknowledged

Cayce's insight into their son's character. The mother immediately wrote to Cayce stating:

> Your reading for [3633] was no surprise to my husband and me. We early saw that such tremendous energy should be set to work, and he is in his third year at a very strict, very religious boarding school. Idleness would destroy him. He must always be in the big world where he will be just a "drop in the bucket"—not the "big frog in a small pond."

Evidently their approach to their son's development was not for the best. Five years later, with her son in his mid-teens, the mother wrote the first of a series of letters describing her son's mental illness. I will simply list some excerpts from this correspondence without comment. Sadly, the letters speak for themselves:

September 1949:
> We are in great distress now over the condition of our only child who has a distressing mental and nervous upset which has not been diagnosed . . .

March 1951:
> The press has been cruel to us in our sorrow, and no doubt you have read of our tragedy. My son [3633], who has been emotionally unbalanced for three years, last Wednesday shot his father and grandmother . . .

August 1951 [addressed to Edgar Cayce's son, Hugh Lynn Cayce]:
> We have some correspondence about my son [3633] and your father's reading for him in which he foretold much that has come to pass. [3633] is now in . . . State Hospital. The doctors have, of course, there and elsewhere in other sanitariums where he has been, labeled his trouble, dementia praecox, schizophrenia, etc.

This last letter was received several years after the death of Edgar Cayce. Mr. Cayce's elder son, Hugh Lynn Cayce, responded with some suggestions for the treatment of schizophrenia from the readings. Naturally, he recommended the Still-Hildreth Osteopathic Sanatorium as a place for receiving the kind of treatments most often advised in such cases.

In June of 1956, the mother reported that her son had been taken to Still-Hildreth:

> . . . and for 2 years [3633] has been there. This is the only place where he has been content and we think it the very best, regardless of price. [3633], with only one backset, has steadily improved there and we have great hopes that he will ultimately recover . . .

We have no further follow-up reports to indicate what the eventual outcome was in this case.

"I Could Kill Them!"

The first reading given for Ms. [3440] was similar to many of the cases of schizophrenia which we have reviewed. This twenty-nine-year-old woman presented with a classical case of schizophrenia. Her condition was characterized by early onset of illness, psychotic symptoms including hallucinations and delusions, dysfunctional interpersonal style, lack of motivation, and cognitive deficits indicative of brain deterioration.

Prior to reading 3440-1, her mother described her condition as:

> . . . an emotional disturbance or frustration coupled with lack of self-confidence, oversensitiveness, lack of vitality and of drive to put things through, all of which has prevented her from finding a satisfactory way of life or realizing her potentialities.

She went on to inquire, "Did any permanent damage result from the two accidental head injuries she suffered in childhood?" Significantly, Cayce did mention a "jar and the injuries to the body" which contributed to her illness. [3440]'s sister summed up the situation by stating, "All of her life [3440] has suffered from an emotional disorder diagnosed as schizophrenia."

As with so many cases of schizophrenia, Cayce cited problems in the nervous systems which resulted from injuries to the body:

> As we find, there are segments in the cerebrospinal [nervous] system where the jar and the injuries to the body have caused the connections between sympathetic and cerebrospi-

nal [nervous] systems to become disturbed. These produce those conditions of nervousness that have long been existent through the body. Also they produce the insomnia, and the upset of the imaginative forces—so that the body becomes easily aggravated, easily tired out, or becomes supersensitive to slights, slurs and the like . . . These repressions and impoverishments produced by pressures at times cause the exaggerated disturbances through various functioning of reflexes. And as there are those areas where coordination between sympathetic and cerebrospinal is disturbed, at times the body apparently is slow in grasping the reflex or the LAW or WHY pertaining to subjects, conditions, things and activities through the associations of the body . . . While these have not necessarily caused permanent injuries, the longer the body has gone without the correction of the impingements existent through the system the greater has become, and greater will become, the disturbances—and the harder it will be to adjust or control them.

Thus, spinal injuries were cited as the basis for the physical abnormalities in the nervous system manifesting as mental and emotional problems. Because it was a long-standing condition, it would be difficult to correct. However, without correction her mental and emotional problems would only become more severe.

The recommended treatments were standard for such cases: osteopathic adjustments, hydrotherapy, electrotherapy, outdoor activities (such as tennis, golf, horseback riding), and a well-balanced diet (with "not too many sugars and starches").

She was also encouraged to study art and music. However, Cayce suggested a unique approach to developing these abilities:

Meditate on these. For, you can even learn to sing and play the piano and never sing a note or touch a piano—in the mind! and then you can put it into practice when the body is better attuned. For music and art must come from the soul, to be worthwhile.

Without mentioning it in this first reading, Cayce was encouraging this person to practice some activities in which she had excelled in a past life. In reading 3440-2, a life reading, he acknowledged latent talents in these areas derived from previous existences. In this life reading, he also focused on numerous destructive patterns which had dominated certain lifetimes:

> Then we find there are urges latent and manifested in the personalities of the entity. When there is taken into consideration a composite of the experiences in other realms of consciousness and in the three-dimensional or earth plane consciousness, we find:
>
> The entity oft tends to become a bit pessimistic and to blame someone else. This is not well. For every tub, yes every cup, must sit upon its own bottom, its own legs . . .
>
> While the entity is supersensitive and at times little disappointments, fears, doubts, and even an upset liver may cause moods—even the shedding of tears, we find that these, too, may be met in the spiritual aspirations and desires of the body.
>
> Know that with what measure you mete it is measured to you.
>
> If you would have friends, be friendly. If you would even have fun, make fun for someone else.
>
> Read the comic papers; not as to become sarcastic, no—but remember, ever, even thy Master, Jesus, could laugh in the face of the cross. Can ye find a better example?
>
> Then see the joy, even in sorrow. See the pleasure that may even come with pain.
>
> These are mostly matters of the mind. For mind is ever the builder. As you think in your heart, so are you . . .
>
> As to appearances in the earth, these have been quite varied and have brought the experiences indicated, in that it is self the entity is meeting. Be not overanxious, but be anxious about thy relationships to thy Maker.

The expression "it is self the entity [or soul] is meeting" marks the karmic dimension to her current problems. Cayce went on to describe four past lives which were strongly influencing the present. Two lives were particularly relevant to [3440]'s mental and emotional problems:

> Before this the entity was in the land of the present nativity during the early settlings, when there were those journeyings from parts of Virginia, Tennessee, to the western land.
>
> The entity was among those who aided in settling in the

land, yet little spites brought those things that made for jealousies, anger, and violence. Thus the moods of the entity that come from that experience.

The name then was Charlotte Price. The entity physically gained, was mentally disturbed and spiritually angered.

Turn those abilities into love. For upon that sign of love, on the opposite side is written hate. Turn the sign over. Love thy neighbor as thyself. For it is the great commandment which was given by Him, who would give himself a ransom for all: "A new commandment—love one another, even as I have loved you."

Though others may hate, though others may speak unkindly, love thou thy neighbor.

Before that the entity was in the Roman activities when there were those who were persecuted for their faith. The entity was among those of the nobles, or those by whose sign a life was spared or a life was given to the beasts or to the destroyers of the physical bodies.

The entity viewed such more than once, yet these always brought horror—and in the present the thoughts of same, even of war, even of such things. Yet the expression has escaped the entity oft, "I could kill them!" And ye did—by thy very act; not of deed physically, but by the nod of the head and the turn of the thumb.

As was typical in these readings, Cayce went on to list other lives in which [3440] had gained from constructive experiences of service to others. Cayce was not simply interested in dredging up dirty laundry and dumping it in the laps of persons presently suffering the karmic consequences of past misdeeds. Rather, he seemed to be saying that we have a choice. He would typically point to past successes and accomplishments which were also present as latent tendencies. He encouraged the individual to choose to manifest these constructive influences in their present situation.

In the case of [3440], he first pointed out two past lives from which present destructive patterns were being exhibited. Yet, he went on to describe beautiful lives in Judea and Egypt which were as latent possibilities. He encouraged the woman to trust these latent urges to be friendly to others; to express love and foregiveness; to develop latent talents in music and art.

It is uncertain to what degree the recommendations contained in these two readings were followed. Evidently, some of the suggestions were applied. The sister of [3440] wrote to the A.R.E. in 1973 stating: "In recent years [3440] has deteriorated, and I am now her legal guardian. She told me the readings prescribed osteopathy treatments which did her some good, and she wants to resume the treatments."

"This Is a Karmic Condition"

Mr. [3158] had suffered from mental illness since he was thirteen years old. When he was thirty-seven, his sister wrote to Edgar Cayce requesting a reading on his behalf. Her letter indicates that he:

> . . . has suffered more or less with fears and illusions of various kinds—part of the time not able to work at all for lack of mind and nerve strength—part of the time doing light work and odd jobs that require little mental effort and responsibility . . . can't do much learning books. Has [had] two breakdowns, being so tormented in mind that he was hysterical and could not control himself. The last being last year and from which he has only partially recovered. Some doctors say his weakness is a result of self-abuse or masturbation when a boy, others say no. Sometimes I think fear of hell in the next life is partly if not all the cause, and if there is such a thing as a person being possessed of evil spirits I'm almost persuaded that he must be.

Interestingly enough, in regard to the last sentence quoted from her letter, Edgar Cayce did acknowledge that possession was a factor in this case. However we will wait until the next chapter to consider just what Cayce meant by the term and how it was addressed therapeutically.

Two readings were given for this man. The first reading, given on August 16, 1943, traced the mental symptoms to a lesion in the brain:

> As we find, here we have a lesion in the brain centers. This causes not only these spells of lapse of control of the body but the inability for the body to control itself in an emotional manner . . . These as we find are those conditions which disturb, through the inability of proper coordination between sympa-

thetic and cerebrospinal nervous centers. Hence oft the things the body would do seem apparently unable to reach the consciousness. Things the body in itself promises not to do, it does. The voluntary and involuntary reaction or impulse, as carried in the white and gray matter of the nervous systems tends in certain centers to run together and become confusing to the body.

Understandably, the prognosis was not favorable. In fact, it was downright discouraging.

This is a karmic condition. While the body might be benefited, it would require long, persistent and consistent effort on the part of some very loving, very careful individual.

The recommended treatments included osteopathic treatments of the spine, not so much to correct misalignment of the vertebrae, as to stimulate the nerve ganglia. The Wet Cell Battery with gold was also suggested.

On October 1, 1943, the sister wrote again to Edgar Cayce describing her relationship to her brother:

His reading stated that his condition was karmic. I am wondering if our situation is not something very much the same . . . if there is not something we must work out together, perhaps, before either of us can have freedom—for I am tied seemingly as surely as he is in a way. I am all that stands between him and the insane asylum. And in spite of the fact that I can hardly carry the burden I can't get the consent of my mind to give up trying to help him as long as I can keep up and going, though sometimes I get to the place where I can hardly make it. Then, too, I get on his nerves sometimes to the extent that he says he can hardly bear it. Yet there is nothing we can do but stick together it seems. He seems driven to desperation by unseen forces and he in turn worries me almost to death, so to speak, not because he wishes to, but because he does not have strength of mind to control his thoughts and actions. I do sincerely hope that my reading will reveal the cause of our troubles and show us how to solve our problems speedily.

The last sentence refers to a life reading which the sister [3282] was to receive. Readers interested in the interweaving of soul patterns may wish to look further into this fascinating case. I will merely note here that her feeling of karmic linkage to her brother was substantiated by her life reading.

From the physical angle, the sister followed the instructions as best she could and requested a check reading. The second reading was given on February 1, 1944. In it the sister requested a clarification on the karmic aspect of her brother's condition:

Q. In what way is his condition karmic? From this life or another?
A. From what he has brought from other experiences that he meted to others.

As this was not a life reading, the specific past-life events were not described. The second reading did advise an additional form of electrotherapy, the Violet Ray Appliance. This mild form of static electricity was often recommended in cases of possession. This was apparently the situation with [3158] for the reading stated: " . . . if these vibrations are used, there will be less opportunity for the attacks that cause such hallucinations."

The sister was also chided for not applying the Wet Cell Battery exactly as prescribed. She had been adding the ingredients in the wrong order and allowing the plates at the ends of the wires to touch, short-circuiting the appliance. Cayce described the action of the battery for rebuilding nerve tissue stating that it would "build new life and energy in the impulses to the brain and to the body forces."

A few months later she reported: " . . . he is much improved. His mental attitude is much better and he is working harder to help himself, so we are encouraged to expect that he will soon be strong in mind and body." She had considerable trouble obtaining proper treatments and struggled to do the best she could with existing resources. The degree of improvement and long-term outcome in this case is not known.

Some Key Points to Remember

The Cayce material is in essential agreement with other prominent versions of the perennial philosophy which acknowledge the immortality of the soul. Reincarnation is presented as a process of growth whereby individuals are provided opportunities for development. Karma is the principle of cause and effect extended over a series of lifetimes. It is the driving force pushing us toward development.

We have noted that karmic patterns may be associated with hereditary and environmental influences which provide a high probability (some would say certainty) that each person will reap what he or she has sown. Yet, karma is not to be viewed as punishment. A sense of guilt is not required or even helpful in these cases. When the readings speak of karma, love (or the lack of it) is usually the real issue.

We have looked at four case studies in which karma was cited as the source of psychotic symptoms in the present life. The patterns in such cases tend toward early onset of symptoms with a chronic course. The readings especially emphasized the importance of the mental and spiritual aspects of therapy in such cases. However, the basic physical therapies advised in most cases of schizophrenia still played a prominent role.

12

Possession
———◆———

POSSESSION IS A difficult subject to discuss in relation to mental illness due to the atrocities which have been inflicted upon the insane over the centuries in the name of religion. Nevertheless, the Cayce readings explicitly acknowledge the reality of possession in certain cases of insanity. Therefore it is important to understand the precise meaning of possession in the readings.

The readings consistently affirm the concept of continuity of consciousness. Cayce's version parallels many of the other major traditions, particularly from the East. The essence of this view is that we do not proceed immediately after death to some eternal resting place or punishment (be it heaven, hell, or whatever). Instead, the process of evolution toward unity with the Creator continues. This process includes lessons in other "classrooms" which are described in various traditions as "planes of consciousness," "alternate realities," and so forth. The normal progression is to utilize the opportunities for growth and development offered by these other realms before returning to an earthly incarnation to continue the lessons of life here.

Unfortunately, some individuals have such strong attachments to the earth experience that they are unable to detach from the earth dimension at death. They exist in a realm which Cayce describes as the "borderland." These discarnate souls seeking expression in a physical reality, may find expression through persons whose spiritual centers are open to cosmic influences. This opening may result from cases of insanity (e.g., dementia praecox or its modern equivalent schizophrenia), alcoholism, epilepsy, and various other organic disorders. Misdirected attempts at spiritual evolvement (e.g., certain occult practices, obtaining "higher knowledge" without applying it, etc.) may also make a person vulnerable to discarnate influences.

Keep in mind that the readings referred to "definite points" within the body which serve as connections among body, mind, and spirit (the "pineal system"). These interfaces with the soul can be adversely affected by disease, accident, or inappropriate occult practices. Severe weakening of these centers could thus leave the body open to outside influences such as discarnate entities seeking expression in the earth plane. In certain cases, possession was indicated when the afflicted individuals had lost control of themselves and had little, if any, ego strength or sense of personal identity due to the degenerative effects of dementia praecox.

It is important to note that Cayce's use of the word possession in the readings does not denote demonic possession. The intrusive entities were always earthbound spirits seeking expression in the earth plane. Truly, the readings' portrayal of life after death can best be described as a "continuity of consciousness." In other words, patterns of thought and action are carried over into the discarnate state. Interpersonal patterns of "possession" developed during one's earthly life would thus be maintained by earthbound discarnates (e.g., a marriage partner who dominates a spouse, a parent who lives vicariously through an offspring, an employer who controls employees, etc.).

With this in mind, one can appreciate the readings' frequent use of the term influence (e.g., "discarnate influence" or "outside influence," etc.) to describe the manifestation of possession. We all influence each other constantly. We are affected by what others say and do. We cannot help but influence the people we interact with in our daily lives.

Discarnate possession could be viewed in a similar way. The difference is in the manner of influence. The influence comes from within—from the very centers in which the soul connects with the physical body. Cayce stated that discarnates will enter that which has been left open and that any individuals can be influenced in this way if they allow themselves to be.

Possession is not necessarily always a negative experience. Throughout history people of all cultures have sought possession by benevolent spirits and have engaged in rituals and ceremonies for that purpose (e.g., the Holy Spirit in Christianity).

Mediumship is a form of trance possession whereby individuals willingly allow discarnate entities to use their bodies for communication. In this form, possession does not necessarily interfere with an individual's course of life or produce pathological dissociation. It is also time limited so that the individual can resume normal conscious daily living. The prime consideration in this type of possession is the conscious voluntary involvement of the person being possessed. The popularity of spiritualism in the nineteenth century and the current interest in "channeling" are examples of trance possession.

Electrotherapy and hypnotherapy were two of the most common forms of therapy for the treatment of possession in the Cayce readings. Cayce stated that electricity would drive out the discarnate influences. Dr. Wickland was an early twentieth-century psychiatrist who used electrotherapy in conjunction with other techniques (such as persuasion) to encourage the earthbound entities to detach from their hosts and proceed forward in the evolutionary process of soul growth.

The Unquiet Dead by Dr. Fiore is an informative and readable introduction to this subject. Fiore is a clinical psychologist who uses hypnosis to perform "depossession therapy." Her view of possession in relation to schizophrenia is similar to that presented in the Cayce readings: "I do not feel that all schizophrenics are psychotic because of the possibility of possession. I do feel that—in addition to their mental illness—they are undoubtedly possessed. The possession is an extra burden for them."

Numerous clinicians are currently involved in various applications of depossession therapy. Baldwin's work with "spirit releasement therapy" echoes many of the themes developed by Fiore. He goes further by attempting to provide a research format for exploring this subject. His work is scholarly and is highly recommended to readers seeking further information.

Naegeli-Osjord is a Swiss medical doctor who provides assessment criteria for the distinguishing possession from schizophrenia. The range of criteria includes interpersonal contact, presence of phobias, auditory phenomenon, sudden changes in personality, and mediality (mediumism). His discussion of auditory hallucinations will serve as an introduction to his diagnostic procedure.

In the theory of established psychiatry, hallucinations—voices—are, for the most part, considered to be primary symptoms of schizophrenia. In my opinion, this is wrong. We have to consider that "voices" which another person cannot hear are real sensations, but only heard by the individual in the subtle interaction of the anatomic auditory center of the brain. This may be caused by either a very intense personal feeling, or by a being of the ethereal dimensions, a "suffering soul" or a demon. But the existence of an ethereal body is not considered. In my opinion, it is an absolute proof of possession or harassment when these "voices" constantly repeat the same words, for example, "kill yourself" or "you are a fool," for a long time, without stopping.

There is abundant literature in this area and it is not necessary to wade through it since possession is not the primary focus of this book. Rather, this chapter is intended to provide a context from which to consider Cayce's occasional reference to possession in cases of dementia praecox.

Because Cayce's use of the term possession in the readings was not satanic, but more a matter of influence and obsession, the manifestation of this state was closely allied to the symptoms of the mental disorder. In other words, one wouldn't expect a person receiving a psychic reading from Cayce which indicated possession to be exhibiting symptoms and behaviors which are graphically portrayed in innumerable movies about satanic possession (i.e., no rotating heads and vomit). Rather, one might observe a lack of control, periods of unconsciousness, obsessive thought patterns, etc. The correspondence associated with the readings where possession was involved provides vivid and personal accounts of the experience of possession in this context.

There are three Circulating Files and a research bulletin on possession which are available through the A.R.E. Dr. James Windsor has written a brief paper entitled *Commentary on Possession* which provides an excellent overview of possession as noted in the readings. A concise quotation from this work will be provided and interested readers are encouraged to review this insightful paper in its entirety.

> Possession was not a major theme of the Cayce readings. It was mentioned several times, almost as an aside, in cases where the primary concern was either physical or mental health. Possession was presented as a consequence of other problems such as insanity, epilepsy, and alcoholism, rather than a cause. The disease, and resulting weakness, opened the person to the possibility of possession.

William James, widely regarded as the "father of American psychology," researched altered states of consciousness including possession. Although James was perhaps a little hard on the medical profession, his view of this subject is still timely:

> I am not as positive as you are in the belief that the obsessing agency is really demonic individuals. I am perfectly willing to adopt that theory if the facts lend themselves best to it: for who can trace limits to the hierarchies of personal existence in the world? But the lower stages of mere automatism shade off so continuously into the highest supernormal manifestations, through the intermediary ones of imitative hysteria and "suggestibility," that I feel as if no general theory as yet would cover all the facts. So that the most I shall plead for before the neurologists is the recognition of demon possession as a regular "morbid-entity" whose commonest homologue today is the "spirit-control" observed in test-mediumship, and which tends to become the more benignant and less alarmingly, the less pessimistically it is regarded . . . I am convinced that we stand with all these things at the threshold of a long inquiry, of which the end appears as yet to no one, least of all to myself . . . The first thing is to start the medical profession out of its idiotically conceived ignorance of all such matters—matters which have everywhere and at all times played a vital part in human history.

With this background established, let us now look at a few cases from the Cayce material in which possession was linked to schizophrenia.

Some Examples of Possession

Actually we have discussed several cases in earlier chapters where the readings mentioned possession as a factor. For example, in Chapter Two, the case of [282] involved possession. Reading 282-8 described how the "centers" had been opened to "influences from without." Remember that Cayce often portrayed discarnate possession as more a matter of "influence" rather than total psychic domination.

According to the readings, people sometimes make themselves vulnerable to this kind of influence when through intense metaphysical study and meditation the body's centers are opened. Reading 5221-1, given for a fifty-three-year-old woman explicitly cited this unfortunate pattern:

> . . . the body is a supersensitive individual entity who has allowed itself through study, through opening the centers of the body, to become possessed with reflexes and activities outside of itself . . .
>
> Q. How did I happen to pick this up?
> A. . . . the body in its study opened the centers and allowed self to become sensitive to outside influences.
> Q. What is it exactly that assails me?
> A. Outside influences. Discarnate entities.

The correspondence from this woman is fascinating and deserves mentioning. She described poltergeist activities and delusions of persecution:

> Mine is the extraordinary case of being the victim of a degenerate who projects his thought into women for all his intimate pleasures. For many years I was picking up this vibration without comprehending it . . . Later I met the man, a distinguished musician, and I was in even greater distress after that. He kept himself in person before my notice, although I never spent any time in his company, and finally after several years, being unable to get anything of value to him out of me, he collapsed. That was six years ago, and all he has done since . . . [is to] endeavor to extinguish my life. I have learned how to channel out of me to considerable extent the electric current that is formed in me, and so the results are confined to extreme suf-

fering . . . Incidently, I am deeply religious, adding profound metaphysics to a very good orthodox understanding, and have had thousands of Christian Science treatments. They, however, do not treat the man; and, of course, he goes on, gaily on . . . This vile monster has made my existence a veritable hell for a couple of decades.

Questions submitted prior to the reading included: "About three years ago, possibly before, a knocking developed in my room, not always in the same place; what is the explanation? When resisting intrusion, it sometimes rushed out a window like a spirit, rattling and shaking violently the window. Will I be subject to further intrusions of the kind, and if so, how can I protect myself?"

In addition to possession, her reading noted physical problems in the digestive system. Spinal adjustments were recommended along with electrotherapy and suggestive therapeutics. As will be discussed shortly, the use of the Violet Ray Appliance and hypnotic suggestion was commonly recommended in cases of possession.

She became outraged over the reading and expressed her discontent in a series of subsequent letters. Edgar Cayce responded courteously, offering to return her membership fee and so forth. She wrote back stating that "The matter is more awful and terrifying than ever." She described how:

> . . . the "thing" comes in through the feet (mostly, I think), like a sort of sting, but producing a queer tickling or itching, and later the part is actually sore while the stinging is going on, may be hours. This is for your record. Anyone having those queer ticklish-itching feet, beware!

She did not follow the recommended therapies and apparently continued to experience the "intrusions."

The Karmic Connection

Karmic conditions were sometimes linked to possession. For instance, Mr. [3075] was twenty-three years old when his mother wrote to Edgar Cayce seeking help for her son. In a letter dated April 21, 1943, she reported:

> My son is now twenty-three years old. When he was thirteen

he took sick. He seemed to have hallucinations, couldn't stop singing. Our doctor advised sending him to a private sanitarium, which we did. He was there over a year. He improved, but shortly after that he had a relapse, and now for at least twice a year since he was thirteen these attacks have come on.

About two months later, she wrote again stating:

Before he had this last attack, which was about five weeks ago, he was on night watch . . . spotting airplanes. He imagined he missed some and that the F.B.I. were after him. No one could convince him otherwise. He carried on so terribly we had to send him to the McClean Hospital in Waverly, Massachusetts.

Edgar Cayce was able to provide a reading on July 2, 1943. It was a complex case involving a karmic pattern and a physical problem originating during gestation affecting the nervous systems. Hence the case involved both biological and psychological aspects:

As we find, the conditions that disturb this body are as much of a psychological nature as of a pathological nature.

Pathologically [biologically], these would have to do with conditions which existed during the period of gestation.

Psychologically, these have to do with the karma of this body, and those responsible for the physical body.

Hence we have here conditions that at times approach near to that of possession of the mind by external influences, or that very close to the spiritual possession by disincarnate forces.

To be sure, these interpretations would not be accepted by some as an explanation. And yet there will come those days when many will understand and interpret properly . . .

Owing to those conditions which existed in the manner in which coordination is established in the physical reactions between impressions received through sensory system and the reactions upon the reflexes of brain, we find these at times become very much dis-associated. And those impressions received sympathetically, or through vision, through hearing, through sensing by impressions, become the motivative force in the reaction.

At such times possession near takes place.

With the capsule of the inner brain itself, these cause the distortions, the associations with not the normal reflexes but with the impressions received in the suggestive forces.

Cayce's description of this man's problem focused on a "dis-association" or short-circuiting within the brain. This caused a distortion of sensory impressions which were experienced as hallucinations and delusions. The dis-association also opened this man up to "discarnate forces." Cayce recognized that such an explanation would not sit well with the authorities of his day. Yet, he predicted that some day the reality of possession would be widely accepted.

As was typical in cases of possession, Cayce recommended that the Violet Ray Appliance be used in conjunction with hypnosis. He prescribed a gentle spinal massage to follow the electrotherapy. He also recommended that [3075] be "trained in those activities that deal closest with nature . . . close to the soil, and that necessarily would be away from cities." It is unknown whether any of these recommendations were followed in this case.

Another Case Involving Karma and Possession

The case of Mr. [1969] presents a similar pattern of karma and possession. In reading 1969-1, a physical reading, Cayce diagnosed a weakening of the nerve forces accompanied by possession:

In the present environs (this is not meant to be as a disputation), it is not thoroughly understood. For here we have a condition that is as much POSSESSION as a weakening of the nerve forces in the system . . .

In the second reading for this man, a life reading, Cayce traced this man's mental illness to karma from a past life:

Then the entity was in the name of Randall Campbell, bringing in that experience the disturbing forces which in the present are finding expression in the madness within self—as an activity upon the forces in the brain's activity upon the emotions of the body-force itself.

The precise nature of the "madness within self" was not described in this reading. Mr. [1969] was in a state mental hospital at the time of the reading. Apparently he was also heavily sedated.

His first reading diagnosed his case as "split personality." As was noted in a previous chapter, the readings tended to view each person as an entity comprised of various urges and soul patterns which manifested in a particular lifetime as personalities latent and manifest. It would seem that [1969] was experiencing strong psychic bleed-throughs from his previous life experience as a man named Randall Campbell. This would naturally be confusing and disorienting. Perhaps the psychological disturbance resulting from a weak or nonexistent focus in a present identity (combined with the physical problems) constituted a vulnerability making this man open to discarnate possession. From a clinical viewpoint, such a condition might be viewed as a form of psychosis—of being out of touch with reality.

And, as with the case of [3075], Cayce again prescribed electrotherapy with the Violet Ray Appliance and hypnosis. Similarly, Cayce's therapeutic recommendations were ignored by the caretakers of [1969].

Various Forms of Possession

Edgar Cayce used the word possession in various ways. Most often he referred to discarnate possession. However, as we saw in the case of [3421] in Chapter Nine, possession can be a bit more complicated. In that particular case, he described the condition as a "positive possession" in which the woman was possessed by her own thought forms.

The case of [1572] represents another variation on the theme of possession. Mrs. [1572] was fifty years old when she received a reading from Edgar Cayce. She was present for the event and commented beforehand that she suffered from her condition for a long time, but that it was gradually getting worse and her misery was unbearable. She said that she regularly felt a "power" take possession of her, and was bothered with images like tiny dwarfs crawling all over her. Naturally, she couldn't rest. At night when she should be sleeping, she had terrible experiences in which she felt that she was a man wandering in search of someone with whom to gratify sexual desires. Her reading was given on April 18, 1938:

> As has been indicated, much of the disturbance is the incoordination between the cerebrospinal nervous system and the

sympathetic nervous system, or vegetative nerve system. Hence pressures are indicated in the lumbar and the lower dorsal area. These are the areas, then, with the brush end of the cerebrospinal system and the plexus of the lower portion of the abdomen, to produce the convulsions in the activities when the body attempts to rest, or often when the body begins to lose consciousness in sleep. Such disturbances are produced as to excite the activities of the glandular forces as related to the plexus at the pubic bone itself. Thus a great disturbance is caused through the activity of the organs of the pelvis . . . this is the incoordination between the cerebrospinal and the sympathetic nervous system. And as the glandular system is affected as related to the genitive system, and especially affecting directly the center above the puba, there is produced—with the toxic forces in the system—this burning, and the EFFECT of POSSESSION!

Just what Cayce meant by "the EFFECT of POSSESSION" is unclear. Was it simply discarnate possession made possible by the disturbances to the centers in the nervous and glandular systems? Or a similar effect mimicked by the biology of her illness? In other words, was she hallucinating because of an organic condition? We shall never know for certain.

However, treatment recommendations included spinal massage and electrotherapy with the Violet Ray Appliance. As we have seen, these were standard therapies in cases of discarnate possession. At any rate, the woman ignored Cayce's advice and endured her symptoms.

Dementia Praecox and Possession

To conclude this chapter, we will consider two more cases of insanity associated with possession. However, before proceeding with these examples, I want to expand upon a concept that was presented in Chapter Nine. An extended excerpt from reading 281-24 was given in the earlier chapter to convey how the life force moves through the body and how the "centers" or chakras are key points in the system which maintain or regulate this flow. We saw how indiscriminate "opening" of these centers and allowing the raised vibration of the life force (which has been called kundalini) to race through the body can lead to physical and mental symptoms.

Some of these symptoms would be viewed by contemporary mental health clinicians as psychosis. This experience has also been labeled "kundalini crisis." Now I want to share a portion of this reading which elicited the response about dementia praecox and possession. It was a question about whether possession was ever linked to insanity:

Q. In certain types of insanity, is there an etheric body involved? If so, how?

A. Possession.

Let's for the moment use examples that may show what has oft been expressed from here:

There is the physical body, there is the mental body, there is the soul body. They are One, as the Trinity; yet these may find a manner of expression that is individual unto themselves. The body itself finds its own level in its own development. The mind, through anger, may make the body do that which is contrary to the better influences of same; it may make for a change in its environ, its surrounding, contrary to the laws of environment or hereditary forces that are a portion of the *élan vital* [life force] of each manifested body, with the spirit or the soul of the individual.

Then, through pressure upon some portion of the anatomical structure that would make for the disengaging of the natural flow of the mental body through the physical in its relationships to the soul influence, one may be dispossessed of the mind; thus ye say rightly he is "out of his mind."

Or, where there are certain types or characters of disease found in various portions of the body, there is the lack of the necessary *vital* [vitality] for the resuscitating of the energies that carry on through brain structural forces of a given body. Thus disintegration is produced, and ye call it dementia praecox—by the very smoothing of the indentations necessary for the rotary influence or vital force of the spirit within same to find expression. Thus derangements come.

Such, then, become possessed as of hearing voices, because of their closeness to the borderland. Many of these are termed deranged when they may have more of a closeness to the universal than one who may be standing nearby and commenting; yet they are awry when it comes to being normally balanced or healthy for their activity in a material world.

We have reviewed numerous cases in which various forms of "pressure" upon the body's "centers" can disrupt "the natural flow of the mental body through the physical in its relationships to the soul influence." Many of the cases of spinal injury and glandular dysfunction cited in earlier chapters could easily fit this description. In such cases the person might have any number of paranormal experiences including precognition, telepathy, past-life recall, etc. In a sense, the person's consciousness would be opened up to the universal level of reality.

Just as Cayce noted in reading 281-24, in certain cases (such as dementia praecox) the centers have not only been "opened," they may be stuck in that mode due to severe physical pathology. In other words, the physical centers which are the connections to the soul may also serve as connections to other souls. A high level of biological deterioration (dementia) could allow this form of possession.

Ms. [2614] was on the verge of this form of possession when she received a reading from Edgar Cayce. On November 11, 1941, a reading was given that described the source of her ailment:

> These are the result of chemical and glandular reactions in the body; producing a deteriorating reaction in nerve impulses.
>
> Thus the mental aberrations that appear, the hallucination as to lack of desire for associations and activities, faultfinding in self and in environs, as well as those about the body.
>
> If these are allowed to progress they may bring a very detrimental condition—either that of possession or such a deteriorating as to become dementia praecox in its nature.

In other words, just as reading 281-24 had described, there was a breakdown in the nervous systems due to a lack of "resuscitating of the energies that carry on through brain structural forces." As the nerve centers deteriorated, the individual would become open to possession. Actual physical degeneration of brain tissue would eventually ensue, or dementia praecox. Thus possession would become a chronic and habitual state of consciousness for this person.

The association of dementia and possession is common in the readings. While there are many forms of dementia, each involves the basic underlying pathology which Cayce associated with dementia praecox—physical deterioration of the brain centers. When the integrity of these centers is compromised, the soul forces cannot maintain their normal contact with the body. Other souls, discarnate souls, may have access through these centers.

The final case study in this chapter is a case in which the readings state that the level of deterioration had reached the stage of dementia praecox and possession. Ms. [3315] was forty years old when she received a reading. Her husband's request for a reading included this background information:

> The condition, now of some years standing, concerns my wife, [3315]. She is a confirmed alcoholic, and everything that local medicine can do, has been done. Part of these treatments have been with her cooperation and part without. It now—after the exhaustion of all aid but yours—becomes a matter of help from you, if a separation (by advice of reputable psychiatrists) is the least that must follow or, more seriously still, permanent institutionalizing.

Reading 3315-1, which follows, offered little hope for this woman.

> The conditions here, as we find, have been so aggravated by animosities, and by hates, that we have a deterioration in the nerve force along the spinal system; so that this is dementia— and now possession, such that this may appear near to hopeless in this experience.
>
> Through the application of low electrical forces as shocks to the body, with patience, care, persistence, there may be aid—if those responsible are active in keeping with divine approbation.
>
> Without these, little may be accomplished.
>
> We refer to the short-wave electrical treatment.
>
> Ready for questions.
>
> Q. What was the original cause, or what brought about this condition?
>
> A. Changes in the glandular system, and then aggravated by animosities and hate.
>
> Q. What can be done if patient is not cooperative?
>
> A. Nothing. But do these things.
>
> Q. How often should the electrical treatment be given?
>
> A. At least once a week until there is almost exhaustion to the body, and then there can be the separation—for, with electricity, dissuasion may be used on those influences about the

body. But there must then be applied love, care, and prayer. We are through with this reading.

Apparently, as with the previous case, the glandular systems were not secreting the hormones required to maintain the nervous systems. A physical deterioration resulted which was exacerbated by "animosities and hate." Possession was a natural consequence of the physical and psychological pathology.

Interestingly, alcoholism was one of several conditions which were most frequently associated with possession in the readings. Also note the reasoning for providing the electrotherapy. As with most of the cases which we have examined, this intervention was advised to drive out the "influences about the body."

From a therapeutic standpoint, I want to re-enforce the significance of the Violet Ray treatments. In reading 2863-1 Cayce recommended that the Violet Ray Appliance be used over the "centers that will prevent any form of possession or impression from the psychic forces outside the body." In my research into the readings on schizophrenia, I noticed that in every case in which Edgar Cayce recommended the Violet Ray Appliance, possession was mentioned as a factor. His reasoning was simple. This form of electrical energy makes it difficult, if not impossible, for discarnate souls to make the connection through the body's centers, even in cases of dementia praecox where these centers are in a deteriorated state.

Some Key Points to Remember

Throughout the centuries, possession in its myriad forms has been associated with insanity. In our modern culture, we tend to discount such explanations as primitive superstitions.

Yet, from the standpoint of the Cayce readings, possession is a reality. The reasoning is that we are eternal beings, or souls, who inhabit physical bodies in reincarnational cycles. At any given time, there are many souls who are not incarnated in human form. For various reasons, some souls become "earth bound" and desire expression and sensory experience which only a physical body can provide. Because the body/soul connection is maintained at certain anatomical "centers" within the physical body, these centers (under certain circumstances) may become accessible to discarnate souls seeking a means of expression and sensory experience.

In this chapter, we have reviewed several cases in which the centers were carelessly made accessible (or "opened") allowing discarnate influence. Intense (but misdirected) metaphysical study was a common cause of such vulnerability cited in such cases. The psychotic symptoms which resulted (which would likely be diagnosed by a modern psychiatrist as hallucinations and delusions) are common in certain forms of schizophrenia.

The last two case studies we considered presented a different pattern. The physical deterioration of the nerve centers in the brain (dementia praecox) compromised the soul's connection to the body providing discarnate entities a channel of influence.

In the next chapter, we will consider the next stage in this degenerative process of dementia praecox. When the deterioration in the nerve centers is too extensive to allow a viable connection, the soul itself may depart its house of clay.

13

Departure of the Soul

◆

THERE ARE A couple of examples in the Cayce material where the readings state that the soul's connections to the body had been severed. The case of [5344] is a prime example of soul departure. Reading 5344-1 was given on July 15, 1944. The brevity of the reading could be attributed to the hopelessness of the case as well as to the date on which it was given (only a few months before Cayce's death in 1945):

Yes, we have the body, [5344].

There has already been departure of the soul, which only waits by here. We have the physical being but the control of same only needs the care, the attention, the greater love which may be shown in and under the circumstances, which will give the best conditions for this body. For already there are those weakenings so of the centers of the cerebrospinal system that no physical help, as we find, may be administered, only the mental or soul help as will be a part of the mental or super-conscious self.

This condition has come from pressures which caused dementia praecox.

We are through with this reading.

[5344] was only thirty-five years old when this reading was given. Prior to the reading, her father stated that she had a nervous breakdown about a year before and was in a mental institution. He noted that "her mind is impaired to such an extent that she is not responsible."

Cayce's enigmatic statement that "There has already been departure of the soul, which only waits by here" makes one wonder just where Cayce's consciousness was located during this reading. In other readings, he speaks of the "borderland" as a transitional dimension of consciousness in which souls might reside during the interlife periods. Perhaps he is speaking of the borderland in reading 5344-1.

One might also wonder just how the body of Mrs. [5344] would have appeared in such a "soul-less" state. Would she have given the appearance of being in a deep catatonic stupor? Or perhaps she might have been slightly more animated yet still rather more mechanical than human? For example, certain learned or rote responses might still be given to common stimuli; as if the nervous system would carry on as best it could with repetitious patterns of behavior. Such an individual would naturally appear to be out of control and not responsible for their actions. Some mental health professionals have noted these patterns in chronic cases of schizophrenia. Such patients have been said to resemble a "burned-out shell" of a person. When looking into that individual's eyes, one might get the feeling that "nobody's home."

From Cayce's perspective, soul departure does not necessarily involve death. His readings indicate that the soul may leave the body for any number of reasons. In fact, one reading stated that we all regularly experience such out-of-body excursions each night during sleep. The difference being, that in such natural soul departures the connections are maintained through the centers in the body. The soul is able to return and continue its earthly existence. In the case of [5344], the connecting centers in the nervous system had deteriorated to the point of severing the soul's connection to the body. The departure was a one-way trip.

However, Cayce recommended that the body be cared for properly and shown love and kindness. While the soul had departed, it was still aware and sensitive to the "fruits of the spirit" and would gain from the experience of such manifested love. In such cases, prayer for the departed soul was usually suggested. The case of Mrs. [586] was of a similar nature. At the time of her reading, she was incarcerated in the Harlem Valley State Hospital suffering from insanity. Cayce observed:

> For there is much that many would study in such a case departed from the surroundings of this body... The coordination has been severed between that which is of the physical-physical [nerve and glands] and the mental and spiritual activities as a unit. As we find, little may be added, save for the comfort of this body.

In many readings, Cayce actually describes earthly incarnation by using a triune model. He said that each of us is an "entity" made up of a physical body, a mental body, and a spiritual body. The coordination of these three aspects is maintained through definite anatomical centers in the physical body. The connection among these "bodies" or aspects of the whole self is maintained primarily through the nervous systems and endocrine glands which we have mentioned in previous chapters addressing both the biological and the transpersonal dimensions of schizophrenia. Maintaining the health and integrity of these key biological systems was crucial to maintaining mental health in both the curative and preventative treatments advocated by Edgar Cayce.

Some Key Points to Remember

Soul departure was not commonly cited in the readings on schizophrenia. I would not want anyone to get the idea that such an extreme fate was necessarily predetermined for persons suffering from chronic psychosis.

Still, to leave out this aspect of Cayce's perspective would not be appropriate either. For after all, soul departure is perhaps the ultimate transpersonal experience. Unfortunately, in the cases of [5344] and [586], this severance of body and soul was premature.

14

Looking Back—Looking Ahead

◆

SCHIZOPHRENIA, AS IT is currently defined, is a complex and variable illness. Most likely, it is actually a group of related disorders. Or if it is a single pathological entity, there are probably numerous causes. The connecting link within this considerable variability is some form of brain pathology. Without doubt, the characteristic symptoms of schizophrenia are somehow associated with problems in the nerves of the brain.

We can feel certain of this fact because of the momentous gains that have been made in recent decades in the field of biological psychiatry. Brain scan technology clearly shows that many persons suffering from schizophrenia also have abnormalities in the brain.

The effectiveness of the antipsychotic medications lends further credence to this biological emphasis. It is clear that these powerful drugs can effectively suppress certain psychotic symptoms in many individuals suffering from schizophrenia.

Yet, we still have a long way to go. Schizophrenia remains an incurable illness of unknown causation. The drugs may suppress some symptoms and not others. They may help some people and be completely ineffective for other individuals. The side effects from these medications are often quite distressing. If the medications are stopped, the symptoms usually return. Even with effective drug therapy, many individuals will still experience relapses requiring hospitalization.

In the area of causation we find a similar pattern of hopefulness clouded by failures. The most common shortcomings are failures of replication in scientific studies. One study may produce remarkable evidence on some aspect of schizophrenia only to be followed by other studies which fail to support the findings. As we have noted, this is exactly what one might expect if the diagnosis of schizophrenia does actually include various diverse subgroups.

However, even with this considerable variability, certain findings are particularly noteworthy. The role of heredity stands out as one of the most consistent areas of research. Retrospective studies of blood relatives who suffer from schizophrenia clearly show that genetic factors are involved in many cases of this illness. These studies also show that this is not the whole story. For even with identical twins, when one sibling is afflicted, the other has only about a fifty percent chance of also developing schizophrenia. Some theorists have advanced the concept of diathesis/stress to account for this genetic variability. In other words heredity, of itself, may not always be enough to cause schizophrenia. Some other causative factor, a stressor, must also be present to bring about the disorder.

There is also considerable scientific evidence indicating that there is often some form of incoordination between the central and autonomic nervous systems in persons suffering from schizophrenia. We are unsure of the meaning of this finding. Some researchers have linked this nervous system incoordination to pregnancy and birth complications (PBCs). In such cases, perhaps some form of birth trauma affects autonomic nervous system functioning making the individual vulnerable to developing schizophrenia.

All of the above research findings and theoretical models support the current medical model of schizophrenia. Ironically, this strong biological emphasis is actually only a rediscovery. During the early years of the twentieth century a group of biological psychiatrists led by Emil Kraepelin had already laid the foundation for this viewpoint. Kraepelin championed the term dementia praecox as the diagnostic category for what we now call schizophrenia. Literally, dementia praecox meant premature brain degeneration.

We have seen that Edgar Cayce gave numerous readings for persons suffering from various forms of dementia praecox. While these readings were given decades before modern biological research into schizophrenia, many contemporary findings were predicted by Cayce. He described the deterioration of the brain, incoordination between the central and autonomic nervous systems, the importance of hereditary factors, the presence of birth trauma in certain cases, and many other significant physiological aspects of schizophrenia.

However he went beyond our narrow contemporary perspective to take a more expansive view of the problem. Even at a biological level, he preferred to take the whole body into consideration in diagnosing the illness and prescribing treatments. The brain does not exist in isolation. It requires the constant support of the body's organs for nutrition and removal of wastes. When these key processes are compromised, the brain suffers.

As we have seen, Cayce implicated a variety of physical factors involved in the development of schizophrenia. Spinal injuries and glandular dysfunctions were at the top of the list. Other stressors such as destructive mental patterns and traumatic life experiences may have also contributed to the psychopathology in certain cases.

The Transpersonal Aspects of Schizophrenia

We have also seen that Cayce's perspective is expansive in other directions beyond the physical body. Each person is viewed as an entity; as an interaction among physical, mental, and spiritual attributes. Cayce even went so far as to talk of the physical body, the mental body, and the spiritual body. This triune model of the self makes possible a broader view of the human condition—a view we have labeled the transpersonal perspective. The transpersonal realm addresses issues beyond the sense of personal self and material reality.

The transpersonal perspective is part of a larger conceptual framework known as the perennial philosophy. The perennial philosophy is a collection of ideas which are universal in the human experience. In other words, in virtually all cultures throughout the ages, certain central themes are present. One of the most basic tenants of the perennial philosophy is the continuity of consciousness. In essence, we are all immortal beings. Life on earth is only one brief chapter in the story of the soul.

The second part of this book focused on some of the most prominent elements of the transpersonal perspective. Central to this consideration, was the idea that the nonmaterial aspects of the self connected to the physical body at definite anatomical centers. The endocrine glands (particularly the pineal and lyden) and the major plexus of the nervous systems were cited as the key centers. Disruption of these centers was a prominent theme in the first part of this book—most notably in the many instances of spinal injury and pelvic disorders. Hence some transpersonal features may be expected in cases involving biological causation, of any source or type.

We have reviewed numerous case studies involving important transpersonal experiences such as kundalini crisis, reincarnational bleed-throughs, karma, possession, and soul departure. These transpersonal elements help us to understand the context of schizophrenia. This context is the same for all human experience—it is the story of the soul making its way through eternity, finding its way back to its source.

By including the transpersonal realm in our understanding of schizophrenia, we do complicate this already complex subject in certain respects. Most notably, the line of demarcation between what is real and unreal (the domain of psychosis) can sometimes become blurred or even nonexistent.

Personally, I don't see this as a problem. It only makes one more sensitive to other people's experience and respectful of their perspective (however crazy it may seem). It usually results in a sense of sacredness, even in this most devastating mental illness. However, if your primary interest is in sticking people in rigid diagnostic boxes so that you can treat them as a mass rather than as individuals, the transpersonal aspects of schizophrenia can be a problem.

Clinical Implications

One of the most important implications of Cayce's perspective is the need to treat people as individuals, regardless of their condition or medical diagnosis. This becomes apparent, if for no other reason, when one recognizes the variability that exists in schizophrenia.

Edgar Cayce was able to maintain this focus on the individual because he saw each person as a triune entity comprised of physical, mental, and spiritual attributes. This comprehensive outlook has been called holism.

Current clinical models used in treating schizophrenia are beginning to recognize the necessity of treating the whole person. In addition to the biological emphasis of drug therapy, other interventions such as psychosocial rehabilitation have been added to address these other aspects of the disorder. The modern terminology for this more integrated approach to treating mental illness is the "biopsychosocial" model of treatment. Call it what you will, it is definitely an improvement.

It is also significant that Edgar Cayce foresaw the need for integrative treatment. The numerous case studies which we have reviewed attest to Cayce's integrated approach. The careful blending of physical, mental, and spiritual modalities was a hallmark of Cayce's holistic method.

Furthermore his therapeutic recommendations usually included relatively natural, safe treatments. These treatments were directed at cure by removal of cause. They focused on helping the body to heal itself rather than simply providing symptomatic relief by overwhelming the body's nervous system (as modern drugs do).

And yet, Cayce was realistic about the relevance of certain allopathic treatments such as drugs and surgery. He saw each person as an individual and prescribed the appropriate treatment in each case. Sometimes he recommended some fairly strong interventions such as surgery, shock therapy, and powerful sedative medications.

He made frequent referrals to various health care professionals including osteopaths, chiropractors, and massage therapists. In chronic or acute cases, he often suggested that the individual be taken to the Still-Hildreth Osteopathic Sanatorium for treatment. We have noted the philosophy, therapeutic techniques, and clinical outcome espoused by this and other similar institutions of that era.

The real question remains, is the information in the Cayce readings in any way relevant to our current understanding and treatment of schizophrenia? The only way to answer this question is by applying the information. In my private practice, I have seen sufficient improvement in a number of cases of mental illness, including schizophrenia, to support my belief that the readings do have something worthwhile to offer in the contemporary clinical setting.

On the other hand, I am fully appreciative of the difficulty of applying this information within the formal mental health system. I will never forget an experience I had while doing my practicum experience in graduate school. As part of my practicum, I was allowed to accompany the head psychiatrist during his rounds at the community hospitals. Almost every morning, the doctor would inter-

view the patients at each facility. While attending one of these inter-
views, I heard a woman telling the doctor about her voices and how
they were able to predict the future. She went on to describe how
the voices told her several months previously that she would leave
California and move to Illinois. The voices even gave her the name
of her future case manager in the Illinois mental health system. Several months later she found herself living in Illinois having a psychotic episode. Naturally, she was promptly hospitalized. According
to her, the voices had been entirely accurate in predicting the name
(first and last) of her new case manager whom she had never met or
heard of prior to coming to Illinois. When she reported this information to the doctor, she sincerely asked, "Doc, am I crazy or what?"
Without hesitation the psychiatrist responded, "Yeah, you're crazy."
End of discussion. As a consequence of her honest admission of an
apparent transpersonal experience, she had her antipsychotic
medication increased.

Although I recognized the transpersonal features in this case, I
also realized that I could not say anything to validate her "hallucinations and delusions." Any sympathy expressed toward her version
of reality would have jeopardized my practicum placement—perhaps my graduate education. There is little room for alternative interpretations of psychotic symptoms in most mainstream mental
health programs. To cross this line can amount to professional sui-
cide.

Since this initial exposure to the chasm between the transpersonal and the clinical, I have observed numerous other similar
examples while working in the mental health system. When working with a person who is having psychotic symptoms, I sometimes
have the feeling that I am witnessing a transpersonal drama being
played out before me. It may be a kundalini type experience or
perhaps the situation has the quality of karma, possession, or a past-
life bleed-through into consciousness. Other than listening sympathetically and trying to be helpful, there is little that I can do as a
mental health professional in that setting.

On the other hand, as a private practitioner, I usually feel a deep
sense of gratification when a client feels safe enough to share
transpersonal experiences. It is usually helpful to share my view that
many of the great mystics throughout the ages have had similar experiences. The client often conveys an expression of great relief and
a sense of self-acceptance. I am willing to accept the persons for
who they are, including their version of reality. I don't necessarily

have to believe it for myself, but I think it important to honor the individuals and their experience.

In such cases, the therapeutic focus is on how to apply the person's perceptions and beliefs. Remember that Edgar Cayce warned that any type of transpersonal experience should produce some benefit. The person was to apply the experience to make life better for self and others. Failure in constructive application was a real danger. So while acknowledging that certain psychotic symptoms may have some worth, I challenge the persons to constructively apply the experience. If they can't do this, I suggest that they find ways to stop the intrusions. This principle holds true for any type of transpersonal experience, whether of a schizophrenic nature or otherwise.

As to the question of whether to utilize modern medications used to treat mental illness, I take a similar stance as Edgar Cayce. In certain cases, Cayce would prescribe very powerful drugs to help a suffering individual through a crisis. This was particularly true if the person's behaviors represented a danger to self or others. In such cases, he would usually suggest that the medication levels be gradually decreased as the condition stabilized and the therapeutic effects of some of the more natural therapies became apparent.

While it is impossible to say exactly how Cayce would have viewed modern antipsychotic medications, I think it reasonable (based upon his attitudes about the medications of his era) that he might have favored judicious use of these drugs. However, it is also quite clear that he would have maintained the basic therapeutic principles of "cure by removal of cause" and "healing from within." These principles acknowledge the body's inherent self-healing capacities and the necessity for therapies which assist rather than resist these natural tendencies.

In short, I think that the information in the readings presents a sensible and realistic view on the causes and treatment of schizophrenia. Only clinical application of the principles and techniques presented by Edgar Cayce will determine whether this material can make a significant contribution in this area.

Looking Back–Looking Ahead

In looking back over these case studies in schizophrenia from the Edgar Cayce readings, one can easily recognize the severity of the illness and the difficulty in providing effective treatment. Certainly, the personal devastation caused by the illness could be characterized as broken lives. Sadly, in most of the cases we have reviewed, the apparent outcome was chronic psychosis and lifetime hospitalization in degrading state mental institutions. In a few cases, the suffering individuals were fortunate enough to receive treatment in private facilities such as the Still-Hildreth Osteopathic Sanatorium.

It is not difficult to see why Cayce's therapeutic recommendations were so often ignored in such cases. In the first place, hardly anyone was prepared for the strong emphasis on biological pathology which Cayce consistently maintained. Keep in mind that many of the readings were given during the heyday of psychoanalysis. Mental health professionals were more interested in psychological explanations on the cause and treatment of schizophrenia. Even if a physical cause was suspected, the unusual treatments recommended by Cayce would not have been given any credence by the medical authorities in charge of such cases.

In the few cases in which Cayce's recommendations were followed to any degree, help was usually forthcoming. When the types of treatment recommended by Cayce were followed thoroughly, excellent results were noted. The published findings of the various osteopathic and chiropractic institutions provide documentation of tremendous therapeutic potential of such an approach.

In looking ahead to possible applications of the Cayce material, one can only hope that such programs could be resurrected. A blending of these traditional approaches with the Cayce perspective and modern biopsychosocial models could make a significant contribution to our understanding and treatment of schizophrenia.

In the absence of institutional programs, Cayce's perspective may have relevance at a grassroot level. In cases where the family did not have the resources to be able to send their relatives to facilities such as Still-Hildreth, Cayce would frequently suggest companion therapy as an alternative. We have seen several examples of this application in the case studies we have reviewed.

In the years since Cayce's death, several individuals have applied this mode of treatment in cases of schizophrenia with good results. For those readers interested in a first-person account of modern applications of companion therapy, the A.R.E. has published a Circulating File on schizophrenia which includes Steve Wood's article on his experiences in applying companion therapy with persons suffering from schizophrenia. In a previous work, I have also described a therapeutic model which integrates Cayce's perspective with contemporary mental health resources (see the Appendix: *The Treatment of Schizophrenia: A Holistic Approach Based on the Readings of Edgar Cayce*).

In closing, I can only reiterate my belief that the Cayce information has a great deal to offer us in the understanding and treatment of schizophrenia. Perhaps this unique information can yet make a significant contribution to healing broken lives devastated by this terrible disorder.

Appendix

Resources
◆

THE ASSOCIATION FOR Research and Enlightenment (A.R.E.) is the primary clearinghouse for services, products, and information associated with the psychic readings of Edgar Cayce. Although the A.R.E. does not necessarily provide these resources directly, the organization can provide assistance in locating the retailers, health care professionals, and so forth that individuals would need if they wanted to apply the information in the readings. For A.R.E. members, a series of Circulating Files are available on loan from the A.R.E. Library. These files cover many illnesses including schizophrenia. The phone number for the A.R.E. is (757) 428-3588. The address is:

Association for Research and Enlightenment, Inc.
67th Street and Atlantic Avenue
P.O. Box 595
Virginia Beach, VA 23451-0595

The preceding chapters have included occasional quotations from various sources. The following list is a collection of some of these sources for those individuals who want to pursue these topics further.

Selected List of Books and Papers on Schizophrenia

American Psychiatric Association. (1987). *Diagnostic and statistic manual of mental disorders.* (3rd ed. revised). Washington, DC: Author.

Andreasen, N. C. (1982). Negative vs. positive schizophrenia: Definition and validation. *Archives of General Psychiatry, 39,* 789-794.

Andreasen, N. C. (1985). Positive vs. negative schizophrenia: A critical review. *Schizophrenia Bulletin, 11 (3),* 380-389.

Andreasen, N. C. (1987). The diagnosis of schizophrenia. *Schizophrenia Bulletin, 13 (1),* 9-47.

Arendt, J. (1988). Melatonin. *Clinical Endocrinology, 29,* 205-229.

Axelrod, J. (1974). The pineal gland: A neurochemical transducer. *Science, 184,* 1341-1348.

Baldwin, W. J. (1989). Clinical parapsychology: A new perspective on spirit possession. In K. P. Freeman, M. L. Albertson, & D. S. Ward (eds.), *Proceedings of the Second International Conference on Paranormal Research* (pp. 443-466). Fort Collins, CO: Rocky Mountain Research Institute.

Becker, B. O., & Seldon, B. (1985). *The body electric.* New York, NY: William Morrow and Company, Inc.

Bleuler, E. (1911). *Dementia Praecox or the Group of Schizophrenias.* Translated by J. Zinkin (1950). New York, NY: International Universities Press.

Bro, H. H. (1990). *A seer out of season.* New York, NY: Penguin Books.

Cayce, C. T. (1978, January). Concerning a physical basis for mental illness. Paper presented at the Medical Symposium, A.R.E. Clinic, Phoenix, Arizona. Available as *Child Development Series, No. 9*, A.R.E., Virginia Beach, Va.

Cayce, J. G. (1973). *Osteopathy: Comparative concepts—A. T. Still and Edgar Cayce.* Virginia Beach, VA: Edgar Cayce Foundation.

Dawson, M. E., & Neuchterlein, K. H. (1984). Psychophysiological dysfunctions in the developmental course of schizophrenic disorders. *Schizophrenia Bulletin, 10(2)*, 204-230.

Ebadi, M. (1984). Regulation of the synthesis of melatonin and its significance to neuroendocrinology. In R. J. Reiter (ed.), *The pineal gland* (1-38). New York, NY: Raven Press.

Ebels, I., & Balemans, G. M. (1986). Physiological aspects of pineal functions in mammals. *Physiological Reviews, 66(3)*, 581-605.

Edgar Cayce Foundation (1971). *Basic diet.* Virginia Beach, VA: A.R.E. Press.

Fiore, E. (1987). *The unquiet dead.* New York, NY: Doubleday & Co.

Grady, H. (1988). *Study of the impedance device.* Phoenix, AZ: Fetzer Energy Medicine Research Institute & A.R.E. Medical Clinic.

Grof, C., & Grof, S. (1990). *The stormy search for the self.* Los Angeles, CA: Jeremy P. Tarcher, Inc.

Hildreth, A. G. (1924). Osteopathy in the cure of insanity. *The Western Osteopath, 18(8)*, 7-8.

Hildreth, A. G. (1929). Fifteen years at Still-Hildreth. *The Journal of Osteopathy, 36*, 518-521.

Hildreth, A. G. (1930). Old osteopathy for the cure of insanity. Paper presented in Philadelphia, Pa. Month and occasion of presentation unknown.

Hildreth, A. G. (1938). *The lengthening shadow of Dr. Andrew Taylor Still* (3rd ed.). Kirksville, MO: Osteopathic Enterprises, Inc.

Huxley, A. (1944). *The perennial philosophy.* New York, NY: Harper & Row.

Kieffer, G. (ed.). (1988). *Kundalini for the new age: Selected writings of Gopi Krishna.* New York, NY: Bantam.

Korr, I. (1947). The neural basis of the osteopathic lesion. *Journal of the American Osteopathic Association, 47,* 191-198.

Korr, I. (1948). The emerging concept of the osteopathic lesion. *Journal of the American Osteopathic Association, 48,* 127-138.

Korr, I. (1955a). Clinical significance of the facilitated state. *Journal of the American Osteopathic Association, 54 (5),* 277-282.

Korr, I. (1955b). The concept of facilitation and its origin. *Journal of the American Osteopathic Association, 5 (5),* 265-268.

Korr, I. (ed.). (1970). *The physiologic basis of osteopathic medicine.* The Postgraduate Institute of Osteopathic Medicine and Surgery: Kirksville, MO.

Korr, I. (1976). The spinal cord as organizer of disease processes: Some preliminary perspectives. *Journal of the American Osteopathic Association, 76,* 35-45.

Korr, I. (Ed.). (1978). *The neurobiological mechanisms in manipulative therapy.* New York, NY: Plenum Publishing.

Korr, I. M., Wilkinson, P. N., & Chornock, F. W. (1967). Axonal delivery of neuroplasmic components of muscle cells. *Science, 155 (20),* 342-345.

Kraepelin, E. (1919). *Dementia praecox and paraphrenia.* Translated by R. M. Barclay. New York, NY: Robert E. Krieger Publishing Co., Inc., 1971.

McMillin, D. (1991). *The treatment of schizophrenia: A holistic approach based on the readings of Edgar Cayce.* Virginia Beach, VA: Lifeline Press.

McMillin, D. (1991). *The treatment of depression: A holistic approach based on the readings of Edgar Cayce.* Virginia Beach, VA: Lifeline Press.

McMillin, D. (1992). *Living nightmares: Case studies in anxiety.* Virginia Beach, VA: Lifeline Press.

Mednick, S. A. (1958). A learning theory approach to research in schizophrenia. *Psychological Bulletin, 55,* 316-327.

Mednick, S. A. (1970). Breakdown in individuals at high risk for schizophrenia: Possible predispositional perinatal factors. *Mental Hygiene, 54,* 50-63.

Mednick, S. A., Mura, E., Schulsinger, F., & Mednick, B. (1971). Perinatal conditions and infant development in children with schizophrenic parents. *Social Biology, 18,* 103-113.

Mednick, S. A., & Schulsinger, F. (1965). A longitudinal study of children with a high risk for schizophrenia: A preliminary report. In *Methods and Goals in Human Behavior Genetics* (S. Vandenberg, ed.), pp. 255-296. New York, NY: Academic Press.

Naegeli-Osjord, H. (1989). Possession and exorcism in the light of my personal experience. In K. P. Freeman, M. L. Albertson, & D. S. Ward (eds.), *Proceedings of the Second International Conference on Paranormal Research* (pp. 467-479). Fort Collins, CO: Rocky Mountain Research Institute.

North, C. (1987). *Welcome silence: My triumph over schizophrenia.* New York, NY: Simon and Schuster.

Nuechterlein, K. H., & Dawson, M. E. (1984). A heuristic vulnerability/stress model of schizophrenic episodes. *Schizophrenia Bulletin, 10 (2),* 300-312.

Oesterreich, T. K. (1966). *Possession: Demonical and other among primitive races, in antiquity, the Middle Ages, and modern times.* New York, NY: University Books.

Peterson, B. (ed.). (1979). *The collected papers of Irvin M. Korr.*

Colorado Springs, CO: American Academy of Osteopathy.

Quigley, W. H. (1954). *Case histories of mental illness under chiropractic.* Davenport, IA: Clear View Sanitarium.

Quigley, W. H. (1973). Physiological psychology of chiropractic. In H. S. Schwartz (ed.), *Mental Health and Chiropractic* (pp.113-118). New York, NY: Sessions Publishers.

Quigley, W. H. (1983). Pioneering mental health: Institutional psychiatric care in chiropractic. *Chiropractic History,* 3*(1),* 69-73.

Sannella, L. (1987). *The kundalini experience: Psychosis or transcendence.* Lower Lake, CA: Integral Publishing.

Scheiber, S. C., Cohen, R., Yamamura, H., Novak, R., & Beutler, L. (1981). Dialysis for schizophrenia: An uncontrolled study of 11 patients. *American Journal of Psychiatry, 138,* 662-667.

Still, A. T. (1897). *Autobiography of A. T. Still.* Kirksville, MO: Published by author.

Still, F. M. (1933). Comparison of osteopathic and medical results in dementia praecox. Paper presented at the American Osteopathic Association Convention, Milwaukee, Wisconsin.

Strauss, M. (1985). *Recovering from the new age: Therapies for kundalini crisis.* Unpublished manuscript. There is a copy in the A.R.E. Library reference section.

Sugrue, T. (1942). *There is a river: The story of Edgar Cayce.* Virginia Beach, VA: A.R.E. Press.

White, J. (1990). *Kundalini, evolution and enlightenment.* New York, NY: Paragon House.

Wickland, C. A. (1924). *Thirty years among the dead.* Los Angeles, CA: National Psychological Laboratory.

Wilber, K. (1981). *Up from Eden: A transpersonal view of human evolution.* Boulder, CO: Shambhala.

Windsor, J. C. (1969, January). A holistic theory of mental illness. Paper presented to the Second Annual Symposium of the Research Division of the Edgar Cayce Foundation, Phoenix, Arizona. Included in the *Physician's Reference Notebook,* pp. 244-257, Virginia Beach, VA: A.R.E. Press.

Windsor, J. C. (1989). *Commentary on possession.* Available from the author: P.O. Box 557, Williamsburg, VA 23187.

A.R.E. PRESS

The A.R.E. Press publishes quality books, videos, and audiotapes meant to improve the quality of our readers' lives—personally, professionally, and spiritually. We hope our products support your endeavors to realize your career potential, to enhance your relationships, to improve your health, and to encourage you to make the changes necessary to live a loving, joyful, and fulfilling life.

OF RELATED INTEREST:

Also by David McMillin: A CD-ROM interactive database, *Edgar Cayce on Health and Healing* (Version 2.0), and books on *Alzheimer's Disease and the Dementias: An Alternative Perspective, Principles and Techniques of Nerve Regeneration, Case Studies in Depression, The Treatment of Depression: A Holistic Approach,* and *The Treatment of Schizophrenia: A Holistic Approach.*

You may also be interested in the *Edgar Cayce Handbook for Health Through Drugless Therapy* by Harold J. Reilly & Ruth Brod
ISBN 0-87604-215-9   Paperback   Order #2073 $14.95

or

Physician's Reference Notebook by A.R.E. Associated Physicians (William McGarey, M.D., et al.)
ISBN 0-87604-175-6   Hardcover   Order #322 $24.95

To order the CD-ROM or any of these books or to receive a free catalog, call

1-800-723-1112

Or write

A.R.E. Press
P.O. Box 656
Virginia Beach, VA 23451-0656
(All prices subject to change.)